Elements

Potassium
to Zirconium

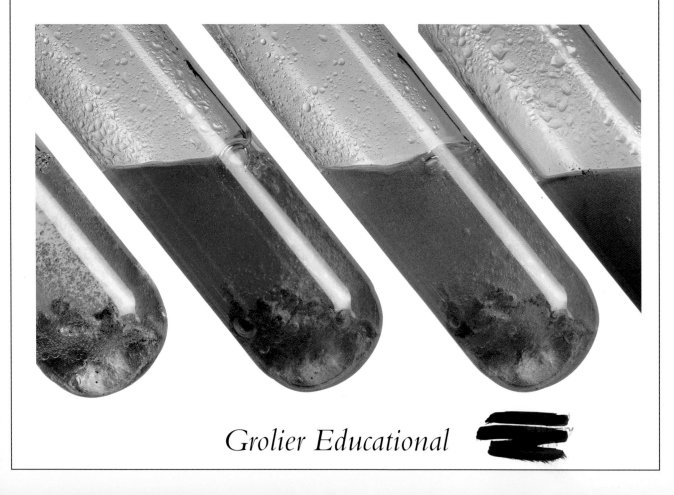

Grolier Educational

How to use this set

The *Elements* set has been carefully developed to help you understand the chemistry of the elements. Volumes 1 to 15 provide an in-depth look at the 32 best-known elements.

Volumes 16 to 18 outline the properties, uses, discovery, technology, geology, and biology of all the elements known up to 118. There is also a key facts table of comparative data for each element.

Volumes 16 to 18 present the elements in alphabetical order, with the full name of the element and its symbol (e.g., americium—Am). Frequently, an element's symbol derives from a different word than its common name. For instance, Ag (from the Latin word *argentum*) is the symbol for silver. To help you find these elements by symbol, the symbols appear alphabetically at the tops of appropriate pages. For example, Ag appears on the page for aluminum and points you to silver: Ag *see* Silver.

At the back of each volume is a glossary and an index to all 18 volumes in the set.

Zirconium oxide is used to make artificial diamonds.

Author
Brian Knapp, BSc, PhD
Project consultant
Keith B. Walshaw, MA, BSc, DPhil
Art Director
Duncan McCrae, BSc
Editors
Mary Sanders, BSc, and Gillian Gatehouse
Special photography
Ian Gledhill
Illustrations
David Woodroffe
Designed and produced by
EARTHSCAPE EDITIONS
Reproduced in Malaysia by
Global Colour Separation
Printed in Hong Kong by
Wing King Tong Company Ltd

First published in the United States in 2002 by Grolier Educational, Sherman Turnpike, Danbury, CT 06816

Copyright © 2002
Atlantic Europe Publishing Company Limited

Cataloging information may be obtained directly from Grolier Educational.

Volumes 1-18 Set ISBN: 0–7172–5674–X
Volumes 16-18 Set ISBN: 0–7172–5675–8
Volume 18 ISBN: 0–7172–5678–2
Library of Congress Number: 95–082222
Dewey: 546—dc21

Acknowledgments
The publishers would like to thank the following for their kind help and advice: *Charles Schotman* and *UKAEA Technology.*

Picture credits
All photographs are from the **Earthscape Editions** photolibrary except the following:
(c=center t=top b=bottom l=left r=right)
UKAEA Technology 46cl.

Title page: The colors associated with four oxidation states of vanadium.

This product is manufactured from sustainable managed forests. For every tree cut down at least one more is planted.

The demonstrations described or illustrated in this book are not for replication. The Publisher cannot accept any responsibility for any accidents or injuries that may result from conducting the experiments described or illustrated in this book.

Contents

Potassium (K)

Element 19. Potassium, a soft, silvery-white, reactive metal, is an element in group 1 (the alkali metals) on the Periodic Table.

Potassium is the seventh most common element on Earth and makes up 1.5% by weight of the Earth's crust. It is found in all living matter.

The pure metal, however, has little direct use.

Potassium is a very reactive metal and is never found in its native state, but always as a compound. It is the least dense metal apart from lithium. It is a very soft metal that can be cut with a knife. For a few moments it is silvery in color, but the surface quickly oxidizes. Potassium metal is normally kept under oil to prevent reaction with air. Potassium reacts so violently with water that it starts to burn. When the element burns, it produces a lilac-colored flame. Potassium alloys with sodium, making an alloy that is liquid at room temperature.

Discovery

Potassium was isolated in 1807 by Sir Humphry Davy, who obtained it through the electrolysis of potassium hydroxide (KOH). It was the first metal he isolated by electrolysis. Potassium was collected at the cathode.

Technology

One of the earliest uses for potassium compounds was in soap. Potassium carbonate was obtained from wood ash by

Key facts...
Name: potassium
Symbol: K, from the Latin *kalium*
Atomic number: 19
Atomic weight: 39.1
Position in Periodic Table: group 1 (1) (alkali metal); period 4
State at room temperature: solid
Color: silvery-white
Density of solid: 0.86 g/cc
Melting point: 63.38°C
Boiling point: 759°C
Origin of name: a combination of the English word *potash* and the Arabic word *qali*, meaning alkali
Shell pattern of electrons: 2–8–8–1

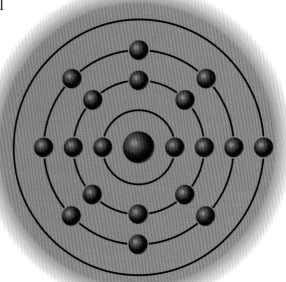

▶ Potassium salts were traditionally obtained from the ashes of trees and other plants. The ash yields potassium carbonate contaminated with a wide variety of other compounds. Potassium is now recovered from coastal salt beds at the same time as brine and also from underground rock deposits.

boiling and then reducing to a powder. This gave rise to the term "pot ash," literally the ash left in the pot. The potash was then mixed with animal fat to make the soap.

One of the main applications of potassium salts is as fertilizers, often as nitrate and sulfate. Potassium nitrate and potassium chlorate go into fireworks. Potassium permanganate is an oxidizing agent and was used to dress wounds. Potassium replaces sodium in low-sodium salt products for people with high blood pressure. Potassium phosphate is a common ingredient in detergents.

▲ Potassium metal reacts violently with water, producing flames and an alkaline solution of potassium hydroxide.

▼ Common minerals such as feldspar contain potassium.

Geology

Potassium makes up about 1.5% by weight of the Earth's crust. Many potassium salts are evaporite deposits, produced by the drying out of saltwater lakes and lagoons. Potassium is much rarer in seawater than sodium.

The dominant mineral in evaporite deposits is potassium chloride (KCl). In many other minerals potassium plays an important part in determining structure and color. Potassium is, for example, found in feldspars, an important mineral in igneous rocks. Carnallite is a potassium-rich metal. Potassium salts are mined at Stassfurt, Germany, and in the United States.

Biology

Potassium is essential for plant growth and animal development. It is found naturally in many soils and is one of the main elements applied in fertilizers.

Potassium plays a vital role in controlling the movement of fluids inside cells and is essential to the working of nerves and the heart. There is no need to add potassium to normal diets because it is in most foods.

For more on potassium, see Volume 2: Sodium and Potassium in the *Elements* set.

Praseodymium (Pr)

Element 59. This silvery-colored, soft and malleable metal is one of the rare-earth metals (lanthanide series) on the Periodic Table. It reacts slowly in air, being more resistant to corrosion in air than europium, lanthanum, cerium, or neodymium, but it does develop a green oxide coating that chips off. To prevent this, it has to be kept under oil or coated in plastic.

Key facts...
Name: praseodymium
Symbol: Pr
Atomic number: 59
Atomic weight: 140.9
Position in Periodic Table: inner transition metal; period 6 (lanthanide series)
State at room temperature: solid
Color: silvery
Density of solid: 6.77 g/cc
Melting point: 931°C
Boiling point: 3,212°C
Origin of name: from the Greek words *prasios* and *didymos*, meaning green twin
Shell pattern of electrons: 2–8–18–21–8–2

Discovery

The discovery was complicated and followed a sequence of isolations. In 1841 Carl Gustaf Mosander extracted the rare earth didymia from lanthana; in 1879 Lecoq de Boisbaudran isolated a new earth, samaria, from didymia obtained from the mineral samarskite. Then in Austria in 1885 Carl Auer von Welsbach, using a sample of the mineral samarskite, found two elements: praseodymium and neodymium. Previously, the mixture of elements had been thought of as a single element and called didymium. Praseodymium is the 37th most abundant element on the Earth's surface.

Technology

It is used as an alloy in high-strength metals. It is also 50% of misch metal, which makes lighter flints, and goes into glass for welder's goggles because it strongly absorbs harmful light from the welding process. It is also used in carbon arc lighting. The colorless salts of praseodymium add a very intense and clean yellow color to glass.

Geology

It is not found as a native element, but in minerals such as monazite (a phosphate) and bastnasite (a carbonate).

Biology

It is not found in living things.

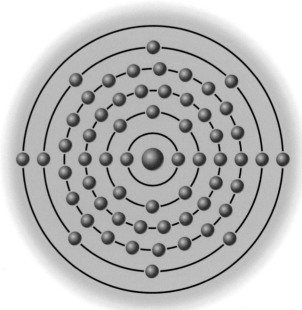

Promethium (Pm)

Element 61. This radioactive metal is one of the rare-earth metals (lanthanides) on the Periodic Table. It is the only rare earth that is not found in nature. Promethium compounds glow (luminesce) pale blue in the dark because of their radioactivity.

Discovery

Promethium was predicted in 1902, but was first identified in 1926. At that time the names illinium and florentium were suggested. It was discovered in 1945 by J. A. Marinsky, L. E. Glendenin, and C. D. Coryell at Oak Ridge, Tennessee. They achieved this by fission of uranium and by neutron bombardment of neodymium. They then named the new element promethium. It was the last of the rare-earth elements to be discovered.

Technology

It is used in very small specialized atomic batteries. Promethium absorbs light and converts it into an electric current. It can also be a beta source for thickness gauges. However, its scarcity prevents it from being widely applied.

Geology

It does not occur in the environment. Despite many searches for it, it seems that promethium does not exist in the Earth's crust. It has, however, been identified in the stars. Promethium has been prepared from nuclear reactor wastes.

Biology

It is not found in living things. However, because of its radioactivity, it is dangerous to handle.

Key facts...

Name: promethium
Symbol: Pm
Atomic number: 61
Atomic weight: 145
Position in Periodic Table: inner transition metal; period 6 (lanthanide series)
State at room temperature: solid
Color: metallic
Density of solid: 7.26 g/cc
Melting point: 1,080°C
Boiling point: 2,460°C
Origin of name: named for Prometheus in Greek mythology, who stole fire from the gods
Shell pattern of electrons: 2–8–18–23–8–2

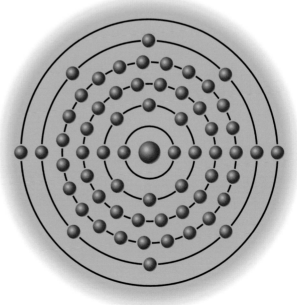

Protactinium (Pa)

Element 91. A radioactive chemical element (originally called protoactinium) in the actinide series on the Periodic Table. It is one of the rarest elements and one of the most expensive to obtain. It is extremely dangerous and can cause radiation damage similar to plutonium. Protactinium is a superconductor at 1.4 degrees above absolute zero.

Key facts...

Name: protactinium
Symbol: Pa
Atomic number: 91
Atomic weight: 231
Position in Periodic Table: inner transition metal; period 7 (actinide series)
State at room temperature: solid
Color: silvery-metallic
Density of solid: 15.37 g/cc
Melting point: 1568°C
Boiling point: 4,000°C
Origin of name: from the Greek word *protos*, meaning first
Shell pattern of electrons: 2–8–18–32–20–9–2

Discovery

It was identified first in 1913 by K. Fajans and O. H. Gohring who named it "brevium." It was then identified again in 1917 by Otto Hahn and Lise Meitner in Germany (who named it protoactinoim) and by Frederick Soddy, John Cranston, and Sir Alexander Fleck in England. However, it was only in 1934 that it was isolated from other elements by Aristid V. Grosse.

Technology

It is used to make uranium–233 for nuclear reactors. It has almost no other use because of its rarity and expensive refining.

Geology

It is found as a minor part of all uranium ores such as pitchblende (uranite, UO_2) because it results from the decay of uranium–238.

Biology

It is not found in living things. However, because it is radioactive, it is harmful if people are exposed to it.

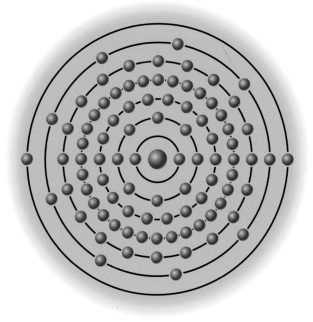

Radium (Ra)

Element 88. This silvery-white metal is the heaviest radioactive element in the alkaline earth metals in group 2 on the Periodic Table. It is a very reactive element. It rapidly tarnishes to black when exposed to the air. Radium decomposes in water.

Radium luminesces (glows in the dark) due to its radioactivity. Radium is over a million times more radioactive than the same amount of uranium.

Key facts...
Name: radium
Symbol: Ra
Atomic number: 88
Atomic weight: 226
Position in Periodic Table: group 2 (2) (alkaline earth metal); period 7
State at room temperature: solid
Color: silvery-white
Density of solid: 5.0 g/cc
Melting point: 700°C
Boiling point: 1,140°C
Origin of name: from the Latin *radius*, meaning ray
Shell pattern of electrons: 2–8–18–32–18–8–2

Discovery

Radium was discovered in France in 1889 by Pierre Curie, Marie Curie, and G. Bémon. This came about when Marie Curie noticed that the radioactivity of pitchblende was up to five times greater than that of the uranium and polonium it contained.

Technology

Radium was used as a mixture with zinc sulfide to make luminous paint. That stopped when the dangers of using radium were recognized. It is now not widely used.

Geology

It occurs with uranium ores such as pitchblende because it is a natural decay product of uranium. It is also found in the mineral monazite.

Biology

It is not found in living things. However, because radiation can destroy cells, radium (which emits gamma rays) found an important use in medicine as a way of treating cancer by focusing radiation on tumors and destroying them. In recent times it has been replaced by cobalt-60.

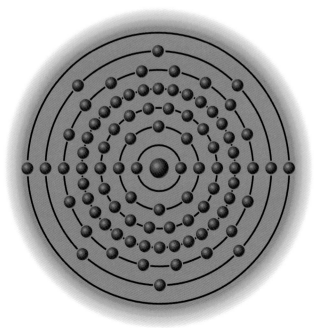

Radon (Rn)

Element 86. It is an inert radioactive gas in group 8, the noble gases, on the Periodic Table. It is the heaviest known gas.

Radon is a colorless, odorless, tasteless gas at room temperature and pressure. However, when cooled below its freezing point (-71°C), solid radon becomes phosphorescent, glowing yellow just below its freezing point, but changing to orange-red at very low temperatures.

Key facts...
Name: radon
Symbol: Rn
Atomic number: 86
Atomic weight: 222
Position in Periodic Table: group 8 (18)
   (noble gases); period 6
State at room temperature: gas
Color: colorless
Density of gas at 20°C: 9.2 g/l
Melting point: -71°C
Boiling point: -62°C
Origin of name: radon was originally called niton, from the Latin word *nitens*, meaning shining. In 1923 the name was changed to radon after the element radium.
Shell pattern of electrons: 2–8–18–32–18–8

Discovery
First observed in 1899 by the British scientists R. B. Owens and Ernest Rutherford.

Technology
Rising levels of radon coming from the ground can be a sign of increased likelihood of an earthquake. Radon is also used in radiation therapy.

Geology
Radon is produced by the radioactive decay of radium. The atmosphere contains small amounts of radon, especially above rocks like granite as a result of seepage from the radioactive decay of uranium in these rocks.

Biology
It is not found in living things. High levels of radon gas may be a health hazard, especially for people who live on areas of granite rock where high levels of radon are produced by the decay of uranium. Radon also occurs in some spring waters.

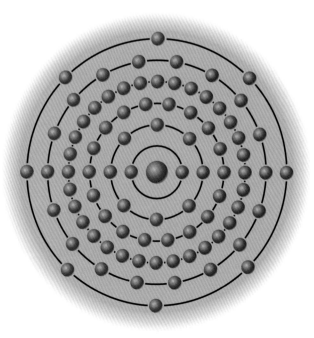

For more on radon, see Volume 1: Hydrogen and the Noble Gases in the *Elements* set.

Rhenium (Re)

Element 75. A very dense, silvery-white, and extremely hard metal belonging to the transition metals on the Periodic Table. It is the densest metal after platinum, iridium, and osmium. It has the highest melting point except for tungsten and carbon.

Discovery

It was predicted in 1871 by Mendeleev as a result of the construction of the Periodic Table. Its properties were supposed to be similar to manganese. However, it was only discovered in 1925 as small amounts in the ore tantalite by the German chemists Ida and Walter Noddack and Otto Carl Berg.

Technology

Used in trace amounts in alloying metals to make them wear resistant. It is used in fountain pen points and similar applications. It resists being pitted by electric sparks and so is an electrical contact material. It is also in lamp filaments, in welding rods, and thermocouples.

Geology

Rhenium does not occur as a native element. It is found in tiny amounts in tantalite, and more substantially in molybdenite, beryllium, and copper sulfide ores. It is obtained as a by-product from the refining of molybdenum ores.

Biology

It is not found in living things.

Key facts...
Name: rhenium
Symbol: Re
Atomic number: 75
Atomic weight: 186.2
Position in Periodic Table: transition metal, group (7) (manganese group); period 6
State at room temperature: solid
Color: silvery-white
Density of solid: 21.5 g/cc
Melting point: 3,180°C
Boiling point: 5,627°C
Origin of name: from the Latin word *Rhenus*, meaning Rhine River
Shell pattern of electrons: 2–8–18–32–13–2

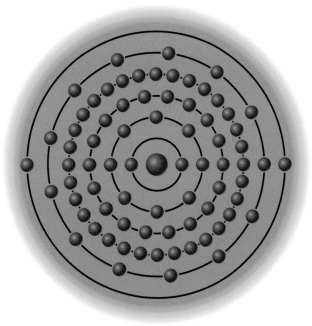

Rhodium (Rh)

Element 45. A rare, brilliantly lustrous, silvery-white member of the transition metals on the Periodic Table. Rhodium is a precious metal and will not tarnish. It melts at a higher temperature than platinum and is less dense. It is also very hard, and resists wear. Rhodium is insoluble in normal acids.

Discovery

Rhodium was discovered by William Hyde Wollaston in England in 1803.

Technology

Its main use is as an alloying metal to make platinum harder. It is often electroplated as a coating on other metals to give a shiny, nontarnishing finish to tableware and jewelry. It makes the reflector surface in searchlight mirrors. It is also used as a catalyst to speed up chemical reactions in carbon chemistry, including motor vehicle exhaust systems. As a hardened alloy it makes bushings in motors and laboratory crucibles.

Geology

It occurs as a native element in tiny quantities in ores containing copper and nickel. Rhodium does not combine in nature to produce many minerals, but sometimes it appears as a natural alloy with platinum, iridium, and osmium. Rhodium is normally obtained as a by-product of the refining of copper and nickel.

Biology

Rhodium is not found in living things.

Key facts...
Name: rhodium
Symbol: Rh
Atomic number: 45
Atomic weight: 102.9
Position in Periodic Table: transition metal, group (9) (cobalt group); period 5. Precious metal
State at room temperature: solid
Color: silvery-white
Density of solid: 12.4 g/cc
Melting point: 1,966°C
Boiling point: 3,727°C
Origin of name: from the Greek word *rhodon*, meaning rose for the red color of some of its compounds such as rhodium chloride
Shell pattern of electrons: 2–8–18–16–1

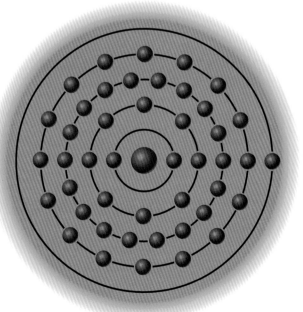

Rubidium (Rb)

Element 37. A member of group 1 (the alkali metals) on the Periodic Table.

Rubidium is a very soft silvery metal that is the second most reactive metal element. Rubidium has to be kept in dry mineral oil or in an atmosphere of hydrogen because it reacts spontaneously in air and water. When it reacts with water, it releases hydrogen gas, which then catches fire. When put in a flame, it turns the flame yellowish-violet.

Rubidium forms amalgams with mercury and alloys with gold, cesium, sodium, and potassium. Rubidium is solid at normal room temperatures, but it can become liquid on a very hot day because its melting point is below 40°C.

Rubidium is a rare element.

Discovery

It was discovered in Germany in 1861 by Robert Bunsen and Gustav Kirchhoff.

Technology

It has a limited range of uses, but does go into photocells and special glass. The age of the solar system (4.6 billion years) has been estimated using the decay of a radioactive isotope of rubidium in a stony meteorite.

Key facts...

Name: rubidium
Symbol: Rb
Atomic number: 37
Atomic weight: 85.47
Position in Periodic Table: group 1 (1) (alkali metal); period 5
State at room temperature: solid
Color: silvery
Density of solid: 1.53 g/cc
Melting point: 38.9°C
Boiling point: 688°C
Origin of name: from the Latin word *rubidius*, meaning dark red after the dark red lines that it produces when looked at through a piece of chemical equipment called a spectrometer
Shell pattern of electrons: 2–8–18–8–1

Geology

It is too reactive to occur as a native element, but appears in minerals that contain potassium, such as biotite and feldspar.

Biology

Rubidium is not found in living things.

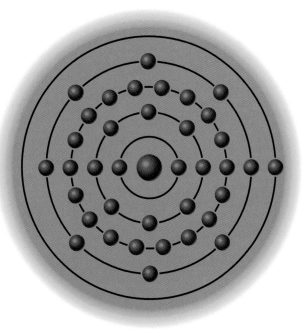

Ruthenium (Ru)

Element 44. This silvery-gray metal, which is easily mistaken for platinum, is one of the precious metals. It is chemically unreactive, does not tarnish, and is not attacked by acids.

Discovery

It was discovered in 1844 by the Russian chemist Karl Karlovich Klaus. It was the part of a platinum ore that did not dissolve in acids.

Technology

Its very high temperature makes it difficult to cast. Because it is brittle, it is difficult to roll or draw into wire.

It makes platinum and palladium alloys harder. Such alloys are in electrical contacts that are subject to much wear and tear. A small amount of ruthenium makes titanium a hundred times more corrosion resistant. In dentistry it makes porcelain-metal restorations. It also goes into fountain pen points and instrument pivots. Ruthenium is also a catalyst that makes chemical reactions go faster.

Geology

Ruthenium does not occur as a native metal. It is usually found in deposits of nonferrous metals, and it is obtained as a by-product from copper and nickel refining.

Biology

Ruthenium is not found in living things. It is not thought to be harmful.

Key facts...
Name: ruthenium
Symbol: Ru
Atomic number: 44
Atomic weight: 101.07
Position in Periodic Table: transition metal, group (8) (iron group); period 5. Precious metal
State at room temperature: solid
Color: silvery-gray
Density of solid: 12.3 g/cc
Melting point: 2,310°C
Boiling point: 3,900°C
Origin of name: from the Latin name *Ruthenia* for part of Ukraine
Shell pattern of electrons: 2–8–18–15–1

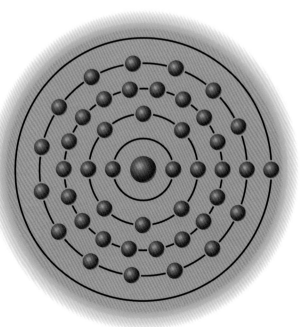

Rutherfordium (Rf)

Element 104. Also previously known as unnilquadium (Unq). It is an artificial radioactive element belonging to the transition metals on the Periodic Table. It was the first transactinide element (that is, an element that lies beyond the actinide series). Although only very tiny amounts have been produced, and no direct evidence is yet available, it is believed to have properties similar to hafnium.

Discovery

It was first discovered in 1964 by Soviet scientists at the Joint Institute for Nuclear Research at Dubna, Russia, and new isotopes were discovered in 1969 at the University of California at Berkeley. The Russians suggested the name kurchatovium (atomic symbol: Ku) for Igor Vasilevich Kurchatov, who was the former head of Soviet nuclear research. American chemists have suggested the new element be named rutherfordium for Ernest R. Rutherford, a New Zealand physicist. The temporary name suggested by the International Union of Pure and Applied Physics was unnilquadium.

Technology

Because so little has yet been obtained, so far it has no uses.

Geology

It does not occur in the environment.

Key facts...

Name: rutherfordium
Symbol: Rf
Atomic number: 104
Atomic weight: 261
Position in Periodic Table: transition metal, group (4) (titanium group); period 7
State at room temperature: solid
Color: unknown
Density: n/a
Melting point: n/a
Boiling point: n/a
Origin of name: originally named kurchatovium, symbol Ku (for Igor Kurchatov, a Soviet nuclear physicist) in 1964. The name rutherfordium was proposed in 1969 in honor of the New Zealand/British physicist Ernest Rutherford. It is the name that has now been internationally recognized.
Shell pattern of electrons: 2–8–18–32–32–10–2

Biology

It does not occur in living things; but since it is radioactive, if it were ever produced in substantial amounts, it would have the potential to be harmful.

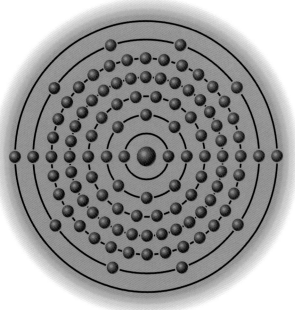

Samarium (Sm)

Element 62. A hard, brittle, silvery-white metal belonging to the rare-earth metals (lanthanides) on the Periodic Table. It does not oxidize quickly and keeps its bright metallic luster well. It catches fire at 150°C. Samarium salts are pale yellow.

Discovery

Samarium was discovered in France in 1853 by Jean-Charles Galinard de Marignac, using a spectrometer (an instrument that detects the type of light given off when a sample of the element is heated). It was isolated from other rare earths in France in 1879 by Paul-Émile Lecoq de Boisbaudran.

Technology

It is used with cobalt to make permanent magnets. This alloy has the highest resistance to demagnetization of any known material. It also absorbs infrared light, makes lasers, and is a catalyst for speeding up reactions. It is also used in the movie industry for carbon-arc lighting. Samarium oxide is used in the control rods of some nuclear reactors.

Geology

It is not found as a native element. It is the 40th most abundant element on the Earth's surface. It appears with other rare-earth elements, but typically in the minerals cerite, gadolinite, monazite, and bastanite.

Biology

Samarium is not found in living things.

Key facts...

Name: samarium
Symbol: Sm
Atomic number: 62
Atomic weight: 150.36
Position in Periodic Table: inner transition metal; period 6 (lanthanide series)
State at room temperature: solid
Color: silvery-white
Density of solid: 7.52 g/cc
Melting point: 1,074°C
Boiling point: 1,794°C
Origin of name: named for the mineral samarskite in which the element is found. The mineral was, in turn, named for a Russian mine official, Colonel Samarski.
Shell pattern of electrons: 2–8–18–24–8–2

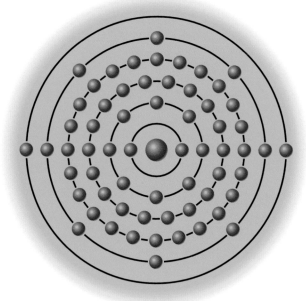

Scandium (Sc)

Element 21. A soft, silvery-white metal belonging to the transition metals on the Periodic Table. It has an unusually low density and high melting point. It oxidizes in air to give a pinkish color. Scandium reacts easily with acids.

Discovery

It was discovered in Sweden in 1879 by Lars Fredrik Nilson. Scandium was one of the first elements to be discovered whose existence and properties had been predicted by the Russian chemist Dmitri Ivanovich Mendeleev from the then newly developed Periodic Table of the elements. He had predicted that its properties would resemble those of boron.

Technology

Scandium is recovered from the processing of uranium ores. Scandium iodide added to mercury vapor lamps provides a high intensity of light similar in color to natural white light. That is important for TV coverage of night-time and indoor sports events.

Geology

It occurs in tiny amounts in a wide range of minerals, but only in substantial amounts in the mineral gadolinite and in ores of tin, tungsten, and uranium. The blue color in beryl may be due to the presence of scandium.

Biology

It is not found in living things. Scandium is believed to represent a health hazard because of its potential toxicity.

Key facts...

Name: scandium
Symbol: Sc
Atomic number: 21
Atomic weight: 44.96
Position in Periodic Table: transition metal, group (3) (scandium group); period 4
State at room temperature: solid
Color: silvery-white
Density of solid: 2.99 g/cc
Melting point: 1,541°C
Boiling point: 2,831°C
Origin of name: from the Latin word *Scandia* meaning Scandinavia. Formerly called ekaboron (symbol Eb) because it had properties resembling boron
Shell pattern of electrons: 2–8–9–2

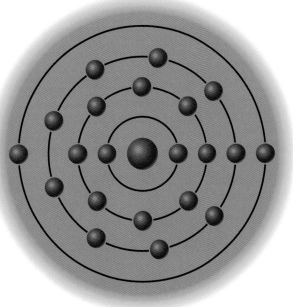

Seaborgium (Sg)

Element 106. Formerly called unnilhexium, it is an artificial, radioactive element belonging to the transition metals on the Periodic Table. It has properties similar to tungsten.

Discovery

It was discovered in 1974 by Georgy N. Flerov at the Joint Institute for Nuclear Research in Dubna, Russia, by bombarding lead-207 and lead-208 with ions of chromium-54. Glenn Seaborg was part of this group, and the element was named in his honor even though an element should not be named after a living person. It was discovered independently by Albert Ghiorso and others at the University of California at Berkeley by bombarding californium-249 with beams of oxygen-18 ions. More recently, scientists at the Paul Scherrer Institute in Switzerland have produced seaborgium using neon atoms to bombard californium isotopes.

Although Glenn Seaborg died in 1999, the final official name for the element remains open to doubt. As a result, it is often referred to simply as "element 106."

Technology

Isotopes of seaborgium exist for less than a second, and no practical uses have so far been found for this element.

Geology

Because it is an artificial element, it does not occur in the environment.

Biology

Seaborgium does not occur in living things. Because it is radioactive, if it were ever produced in significant amounts, it would be a health hazard.

Key facts...

Name: seaborgium (unnilhexium)
Symbol: Sg
Atomic number: 106
Atomic weight: 263
Position in Periodic Table: transition metal, group (6) (chromium group); period 7
State at room temperature: solid
Color: unknown
Density: n/a
Melting point: n/a
Boiling point: n/a
Origin of name: for American nuclear chemist Glenn T. Seaborg.
Shell pattern of electrons: 2–8–17–14–1

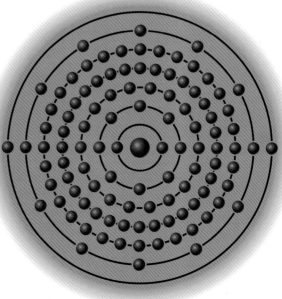

Selenium (Se)

Element 34. Selenium is a metalloid (part way between a metal and a nonmetal) in group 6 (the oxygen group) on the Periodic Table.

It occurs in two forms: one has crystals and is gray, and one is glassy and black when solid and red when in powdered form. The crystalline and glassy forms have different densities and melting points.

It has the unusual property that it conducts electricity much better when light falls on it. It can also convert light into electricity.

Discovery

It was discovered in 1818 by Swedish chemist Jöns Jacob Berzelius.

Technology

It is used in photoelectric cells and solar cells. Selenium can convert a.c. electricity to d.c. and is therefore used in rectifiers. It also makes red enamels and strengthens rubber. It produces an alloy with stainless steels.

Geology

Selenium can occur as a native element associated with native sulfur. It is extracted as a by-product of copper refining. It does not readily form minerals.

Biology

Selenium is an essential trace element and so is a vital part of all diets. However, high levels of selenium can be poisonous. Plants growing in high selenium soils have poisoned grazing animals.

Key facts...
Name: selenium
Symbol: Se
Atomic number: 34
Atomic weight: 78.96
Position in Periodic Table: group 6 (16) (oxygen group; chalcogen); period 4
State at room temperature: solid
Color: red, black, gray
Densities of solids: glassy 4.28 g/cc; gray 4.79 g/cc
Melting points: glassy 50°C; gray 217°C
Boiling point: 685°C
Origin of name: from the Greek word *selene*, meaning moon
Shell pattern of electrons: 2–8–18–6

▼ Selenium is used in photoelectric cells.

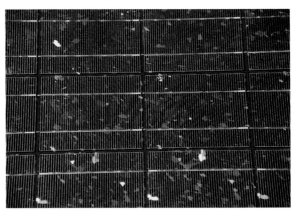

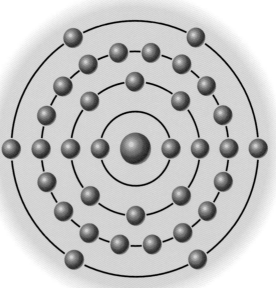

Silicon (Si)

Element 14. Silicon is a metalloid (between a metal and a nonmetal) in group 4 (the carbon group) on the Periodic Table. Silicon has a structure and many properties similar to the diamond form of carbon.

Silicon does not occur uncombined, but always with oxygen as silicates and other minerals. Quartz (SiO_2, silicon dioxide, or silica) is a compound of silicon and oxygen. Sand and clay are also compounds dominated by silica.

Pure silicon is a hard, dark, gray solid. Silicon is unreactive with water or acids. It is the main component in glass.

The atomic structure of silicon has made it a very important semiconductor. It is the basis of silicon chips in computers.

Discovery

Discovered by Jöns Jacob Berzelius in Sweden in 1824.

Technology

One of the main uses of the mineral is as a base for silicon chips in the electronics industry. It is doped with boron, gallium, phosphorus, or arsenic to make a wide range of solid-state devices.

Silica as silicone is a waterproof inert sealer. Silica as sand is used in most buildings. When heated and softened, it can be formed into glass.

Key facts...
Name: silicon
Symbol: Si
Atomic number: 14
Atomic weight: 28.09
Position in Periodic Table: group 4 (14) (carbon group); period 3
State at room temperature: solid
Color: dark gray with a bluish tinge
Density of solid: 2.33 g/cc
Melting point: 1,410°C
Boiling point: 2,355°C
Origin of name: from the Latin word *silicis*, meaning flint
Shell pattern of electrons: 2–8–4

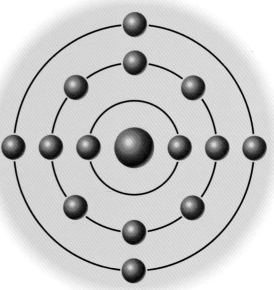

▶ Glass is made from silicates, which in the form of sand are abundant and widespread.

Because of its poor reactivity it is used widely to make containers. Silicon carbide is an important abrasive. It is also an ingredient in steel.

Geology

Silicon is not found as a native element. It mostly forms an oxide that is the common mineral quartz. Forms of quartz include rock crystal, amethyst, agate, flint, jasper, and opal. Other more complex minerals containing substantial amounts of silica include hornblende, feldspar, and mica. Silicon makes up about 28% of the Earth's crust, making it the second most common element in the crust after oxygen.

Biology

Silica is used by some living things to make their skeletons. Birds eat sand because of their need for silicon. The presence of silicon dust can cause a lung inflammation called silicosis.

▲ Silicon is used in computer technology.

▼ Silicates, a combination of silicon and oxygen, form the most widely occuring minerals. This is a piece of agate.

▲ Silicon ceramics are useful because they can sustain high temperatures for long periods without melting. This is a ceramic crucible used in chemistry laboratory demonstrations.

For more on silicon, see Volume 9: Silicon in the *Elements* set.

Silver (Ag)

Element 47. A soft, silvery metal belonging to the transition metals on the Periodic Table.

Silver is one of the precious metals. It is the best conductor of electricity and heat and is also the best-known reflector of light (although this property is lessened because of its tendency to tarnish).

Silver is somewhat harder than gold and can also be bent and beaten into shape. It tarnishes when exposed to ozone or hydrogen sulfide. These gases are present in all air, but most concentrated in industrial cities.

Silver is normally recovered during the processing of lead, copper, and zinc ores.

Key facts...

Name: silver
Symbol: Ag
Atomic number: 47
Atomic weight: 107.88
Position in Periodic Table: transition metal, group (11) (copper group; coinage metal); period 5
State at room temperature: solid
Color: silver
Density of solid: 10.5 g/cc
Melting point: 960.8°C
Boiling point: 2,212°C
Origin of name: from the Anglo-Saxon word *siolfur*, meaning silver. The symbol Ag comes from the Latin word *argentum*, meaning silver.
Shell pattern of electrons: 2–8–18–18–1

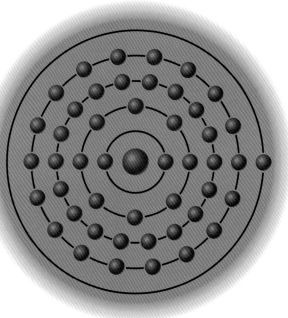

▲ Silver coins have been in existence for thousands of years. This is an example of a Greek tetradrachma showing Apollo. It was minted between 261 and 246 B.C.

Discovery

Known since ancient times.

Technology

Silver is widely used in jewelry (but not in modern "silver" coins). "Sterling silver" makes the best silverware. It is an alloy with 92.5% silver and 7.5% copper. Silver is also alloyed with elements such as nickel to make electrical contacts.

Silver is part of specialized high-capacity silver–zinc and silver–cadmium batteries. It makes mirrors in which the glass keeps the silver from tarnishing (the reflection comes from the back or silvered side of the mirror). Silver salts are part of light-sensitive photographic film.

Geology

Silver occurs in native form. It is widely distributed, but the total in the Earth's crust is relatively small. It occurs in ores that contain other precious metals. The most important ore is silver sulfide.

Biology

Silver does not occur in living things.

▶ Silver is used for many mirrors, either on the surface of a supporting material, or on the back of a sheet of glass to protect it from tarnishing.

◀ Silver deposited on the inside of a round-bottomed flask

▼ Dendritic silver. Native silver, which is tarnishing gray on exposure to the air, set in a mineral groundmass.

▶ Silver metal reacts with hydrogen sulfide gas in the air to produce black silver sulfide.

For more on silver, see Volume 5: Copper, Silver, and Gold in the *Elements* set.

Sodium (Na)

Element 11. A soft, silvery-white metal in group 1 (the alkali metals) on the Periodic Table.

Sodium is the most common alkali metal and the sixth most abundant element on Earth. It is most frequently found as the compound sodium chloride—common salt.

Sodium metal is very reactive. It easily ignites in air. It reacts vigorously with water to release hydrogen (which then may catch fire).

Sodium is widely used to make chemicals and also for yellow sodium vapor lamps. Sodium will form an alloy with potassium.

Key facts...
Name: sodium
Symbol: Na
Atomic number: 11
Atomic weight: 22.98
Position in Periodic Table: group 1 (1) (alkali metal); period 3
State at room temperature: solid
Color: silvery-white
Density of solid: 0.97 g/cc
Hardness: 0.5
Melting point: 98°C
Boiling point: 883°C
Origin of name: a combination of the English word soda and the Latin word for soda, *natrium*. The symbol Na comes from the first two letters of *natrium*.
Shell pattern of electrons: 2–8–1

The cut surface of the sodium pellet has a shiny surface that tarnishes very quickly.

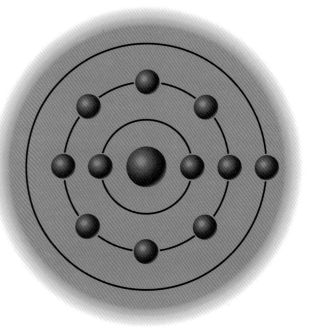

Discovery

Sodium was one of many elements discovered by Sir Humphry Davy during his experiments with electricity. He found sodium in 1807 during the electrical separation (electrolysis) of molten sodium hydroxide, NaOH. Sodium was collected at the cathode.

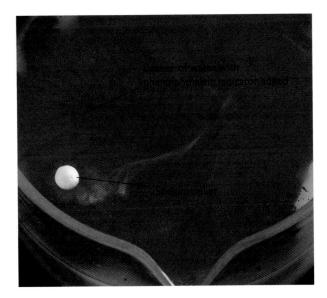

Technology

Sodium metal is hard to use directly because it reacts so readily in air. Sodium was part of the lead compound that was an antiknock ingredient in gasoline in the days before unleaded gas. Its use has now been discontinued in industrial countries. It also helps extract titanium from its chloride ore (sodium and chloride combining to make common salt, while the titanium is left as a free metal).

Sodium also goes into the preparation of organic compounds. Sodium vapor is in the street lamps that give out a characteristic orange glow.

Sodium chloride (common salt) adds flavor to foods and preserves them (it works by absorbing the water in microbes and dehydrating them). Soda ash is sodium carbonate; baking soda is sodium bicarbonate (baking powder); caustic soda is sodium hydroxide, used as a way of removing grease. Sodium salts help in soap making.

Geology

Sodium makes up about 3% of the Earth's crust. Sodium is also found in all stars.

Sodium does not occur as a native metal because it is too reactive. Its compounds are naturally dissolved in seawater and lakes with inland drainage. Inland lakes and coastal lagoons develop very high concentrations of sodium salts as water dries up. In time these salt accumulations form evaporite deposits. The most common mineral in this group is rock salt, sodium chloride, known as the mineral halite. The nitrate is known as Chile saltpeter.

Biology

Sodium is an essential element for life. As an ion it is important in helping substances move across cell walls and so leave the bloodstream. It is also essential for nerve activity.

In animals, sweating results in loss of sodium (as does excessive loss of body fluids during dysentery). Natural diets contain enough sodium for health, but processed foods are high in sodium. As a result, many people consume two to three times their need for sodium. This can result in high blood pressure.

▶ Sea salt, obtained from evaporation, can be produced in large crystals. They are then ground down for use on the table.

For more on sodium, see Volume 2: Sodium and Potassium in the *Elements* set.

Strontium (Sr)

Element 38. A soft, leadlike metal in group 2 (the alkaline-earths) on the Periodic Table. It is softer than calcium and more reactive, decomposing quickly in water. Its silvery surface when freshly cut rapidly tarnishes to a yellow oxide. A powder of strontium ignites spontaneously in air. Strontium compounds turn flames a crimson color.

Key facts...
Name: strontium
Symbol: Sr
Atomic number: 38
Atomic weight: 87.62
Position in Periodic Table: group 2 (2) (alkaline earth metal); period 5
State at room temperature: solid
Color: silvery
Density of solid: 2.54 g/cc
Melting point: 769°C
Boiling point: 1,384°C
Origin of name: named for the village of Strontian in Scotland
Shell pattern of electrons: 2–8–18–8–2

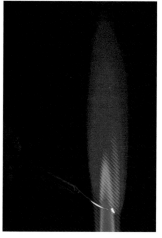

▲ Red strontium flame

Discovery

It was discovered in 1790 by Scottish scientists Adair Crawford and William Cruikshank in a new mineral strontianite (strontium carbonate, $SrCO_3$). Strontium metal was isolated by Sir Humphry Davy using electrical means in 1808.

Technology

Strontium produces the red color in signal flares and fireworks. It is also used in glass for television tubes.

Geology

Strontium is not found as a native element, but mainly in strontianite and also as a result of nuclear explosions.

Biology

Strontium does not occur naturally in living things. However, because strontium and calcium are so similar, and strontium is more reactive, any strontium in the environment will be absorbed by the body, and it will replace calcium in the bones.

Radioactive isotopes of strontium are produced during nuclear explosions, and they are the main health hazard in radioactive fallout. Strontium in the soil from the fallout of the Chernobyl nuclear explosion in 1986 has resulted in many areas in northern Europe being unsuitable for farming.

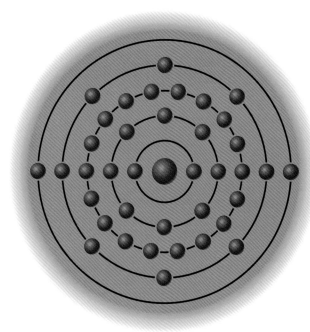

Sulfur (S)

Element 16. This yellow-colored nonmetal (known since ancient times as brimstone) is in group 6 (the oxygen group) on the Periodic Table.

It is one of the most reactive of the elements. It is the ninth most abundant element in the universe and is the third most common element in minerals after oxygen and silicon.

Pure sulfur is a brittle solid that is a poor conductor of electricity and insoluble in water.

Key facts...

Name: sulfur
Symbol: S
Atomic number: 16
Atomic weight: 32.07
Position in Periodic Table: group 6 (16), (oxygen group; chalcogen); period 3
State at room temperature: solid
Color: two forms: lemon yellow and amber
Densities of solids: rhombic form 2.07 g/cc; monoclinic form 1.96 g/cc
Melting point: rhombic form: 112.8°C; monoclinic form: 119°C
Boiling point: 444.6°C
Origin of name: from the Sanskrit word *sulvere*, meaning sulfur; or from the Latin word *sulfurium*, meaning sulfur
Shell pattern of electrons: 2–8–6

Discovery

Known since ancient times.

Technology

Most of the sulfur produced is used to make sulfuric acid, H_2SO_4. It is the most important manufactured chemical in the world. Sulfuric acid is, in turn, used for the manufacture of fertilizers and some plastics. It is also in car batteries as battery acid. Sulfur also helps harden (vulcanize) natural rubber. Sulfur compounds bleach things, especially paper. Sulfur is widely applied as a pesticide and fungicide. Its compounds have many important roles in medicine. Carbon disulfide is an industrial solvent. Gunpowder is a mixture of potassium nitrate, carbon, and sulfur.

◀ Sulfur is usually found in a laboratory as a crumbly yellow powder.

Geology

Sulfur occurs as a native element in two forms, one with rhombic crystals, the other with monoclinic crystals. It is found in native form near volcanoes and hot springs.

It also appears widely as compounds, often in the form of a sulfide compounded with a metal. Galena (lead sulfide, PbS) and pyrite (iron sulfide, FeS) are common minerals.

Gypsum (calcium sulfate, CaS) and barite (barium sulfate, BaS) are found in salt-lake deposits. Sulfur also occurs in underground salt domes and in natural gas and crude oil. They are major sources of the element for industry.

▶ Sulfur compounds form the basis for many drugs such as this one, which is used to assist in the control of a bowel disorder.

▼ This sulfur deposit is around a geyser vent near Rotorua in New Zealand. The needlelike crystals that have formed show a monoclinic structure.

Biology

Sulfur is essential to life and found in proteins, fatty tissues, body fluids, and bones. However, some sulfur gases, particularly hydrogen sulfide, can be poisonous. Sulfur dioxide is a major part of atmospheric pollution and responsible for acid rain. Sulfur dioxide is also used as a food preservative.

Native sulfur is toxic to many bacteria and fungi, and so is widely used in medicines and as a pesticide and fungicide.

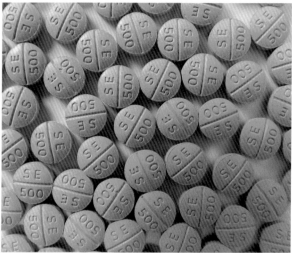

For more on sulfur, see Volume 13: Sulfur in the *Elements* set.

Tantalum (Ta)

Element 73. This rare, very hard, silvery-gray metal is one of the transition metals on the Periodic Table.

It is very dense and has a high melting point (only exceeded by tungsten and rhenium). It can be drawn out into a very fine wire. It resists attack by acids unless heated.

Discovery

It was discovered in 1802 by the Swedish chemist Anders Gustaf Ekeberg, although for a long time people could not tell the difference between niobium and tantalum. It was not until 1907 that pure tantalum was produced.

Technology

Tantalum goes into corrosion-resistant containers and can be used for metal implants because it is not corroded by fluids in the body. It was once made into filaments in light bulbs (now replaced by tungsten). It is found in high-strength alloys such as those needed in aircraft and also in electrical components called capacitors.

Tantalum oxide is part of the glass in camera lenses.

Geology

Tantalum is not found as the native metal but mainly in the mineral tantalite (iron, manganese, tantalum oxide $(Fe,Mn)Ta_2O_6$), which is often found in association with tin ore.

Biology

It is not found in living things.

Key facts...
Name: tantalum
Symbol: Ta
Atomic number: 73
Atomic weight: 180.95
Position in Periodic Table: transition metal, group (5) (vanadium group); period 6
State at room temperature: solid
Color: silvery-gray
Density of solid: 16.6 g/cc
Melting point: 2,996°C
Boiling point: 5,425°C
Origin of name: named after the mythological character Tantalus (the father of Niobe). The name comes from the fact that tantalum and niobium have very similar properties.
Shell pattern of electrons: 2–8–18–32–11–2

▼ Tantalum is used in capacitors.

Technetium (Tc)

Element 43. An artificial radioactive silvery metal that belongs to the transition metals on the Periodic Table. It is not very reactive and tarnishes slowly in air.

It was the first element to be artificially produced (see origin of name). It is used as a fuel in nuclear reactors. All of the isotopes (varieties) of technetium are radioactive.

Discovery

Technetium was incorrectly reported as having been discovered in 1925, at which time it was named masurium. It was actually discovered in Italy in 1937 by Carlo Perrier and Emilio Segrè by bombarding molybdenum with deuteron particles.

Technology

Very small amounts can help steels resist corrosion. Because technetium is radioactive, this protection can only be given to steels in nuclear reactors and other places where shielding from radioactivity is possible. Because technetium-99 comes from the fission of uranium in nuclear reactors, relatively large quantities have now been produced. The element is a very effective corrosion inhibitor for steel and an excellent superconductor below -262°C.

Geology

Minute amounts have been found on Earth in molybdenum and uranium ores. The first isolation was in 1962, when technetium-99 was identified in African pitchblende (a uranium rich ore). However, for all practical purposes it does not exist in the

> **Key facts...**
> Name: technetium
> Symbol: Tc
> Atomic number: 43
> Atomic weight: 99
> Position in Periodic Table: transition metal, group (7) (manganese group); period 5
> State at room temperature: solid
> Color: silvery
> Density of solid: 11.5 g/cc
> Melting point: 2,172°C
> Boiling point: 4,877°C
> Origin of name: from the Greek word *technikos*, meaning artificial
> Shell pattern of electrons: 2–8–18–14–1

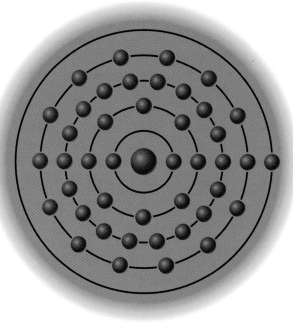

Earth's surface rocks. Special telescopes have detected technetium in stars.

Biology

Because it is an artificially produced element, it is not found in living things. Being radioactive, and having the property of binding to living organic molecules, it has the potential to be useful in medicine under controlled conditions. It is used for taking body images because its half-life is short, and so it is not retained in the body.

Tellurium (Te)

Element 52. A silvery-gray solid with a metallic luster or dark gray powder. It is a brittle metalloid (with properties between a metal and a nonmetal) in group 6 (the oxygen group) on the Periodic Table. It has properties very similar to selenium.

Tellurium is a poor conductor of heat and a moderate conductor of electricity. It burns in air with a blue-green flame. Molten tellurium corrodes iron, copper, and stainless steel.

Discovery

It was discovered in gold ore in 1782 in Romania by Franz Joseph Müller von Reichenstein. It was named by Martin Heinrich Klaproth, who isolated it in 1798.

Technology

Tellurium is a p-type semiconductor. It can be doped with silver, copper, gold, and tin, but it has not been widely used. Tellurium added to copper and stainless steels as an alloy makes it easier to machine these metals. When added to lead, it makes it less susceptible to corrosion by sulfuric acid. Tellurium is also used in blasting caps.

Geology

Tellurium does occur in small amounts as a native element, but usually as gold telluride (calaverite). It is extracted from the muds that are produced during the electrolytic refining of copper. The famous town of Telluride in the Colorado Rockies is named for a deposit of the gold telluride ore.

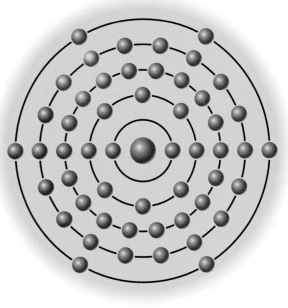

Biology

Tellurium is not found in living things. However, when even tiny amounts are present in the air (as when mining telluride ores), the effect is to make the breath smell like garlic. It is called "tellurium breath" by miners. Its compounds are probably toxic.

Terbium (Tb)

Element 65. A silvery-white metal belonging to the rare-earth metals (lanthanides) on the Periodic Table. It is a soft, easily shaped metal and can be cut with a knife. It oxidizes slowly in air. It is one of the rarest rare earths.

Discovery

It was discovered in Sweden in 1843 by Carl Gustaf Mosander.

Technology

It is used in the form of sodium terbium borate as a laser material. It also can dope semiconductors to make electronic components. Terbium oxide makes green phosphors active when applied to the front of color television tubes. It is likely that it will also find uses in alloys, but techniques for its isolation in significant amounts have only been developed recently, and so there has not been time for this branch of science to be developed.

Geology

Terbium is not found as a native metal, but in very small amounts in monazite sands combined with other rare earths. Small amounts also occur in cerite, gadolinite, xenotime, and euxenite ores. It is about the 58th in abundance in the Earth's surface rocks.

Biology

Terbium is not found in living things.

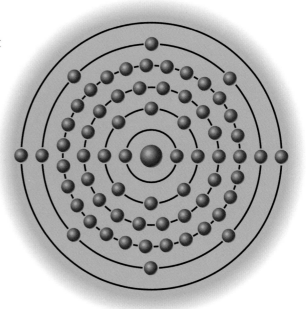

Thallium (Tl)

Element 81. A blue-gray, malleable, leadlike metal that is part of group 3 (the boron group) on the Periodic Table. It rapidly oxidizes in air and develops a thick oxide coating. It is soft enough to be cut by a knife. Thallium salts burn with a bright green flame.

Discovery

It was discovered in England in 1861 by Sir William Crookes. It is the 60th most abundant element on the Earth's surface.

Technology

Thallium sulfate is colorless, odorless, and tasteless. It was once used to kill rodents and insects.

Thallium sulfide changes its electrical properties when exposed to light and so is part of photocells. It can help in producing glasses with a low melting point. Thallium bromide-iodide crystals can detect infrared radiation. It was once combined with mercury in thermometers.

The bright green color produced during burning made it a coloring material in fireworks.

Geology

Thallium does not occur as a native element, and its minerals are rare. Thallium comes from a by-product of refining zinc, lead, and iron. It is most commonly recovered from the dust that rises in the chimney during the smelting of iron pyrites.

Key facts...

Name: thallium
Symbol: Tl
Atomic number: 81
Atomic weight: 204.38
Position in Periodic Table: group 3 (13) (boron group); period 6
State at room temperature: solid
Color: blue-gray
Density of solid: 11.85 g/cc
Melting point: 303.5°C
Boiling point: 1,457°C
Origin of name: from the Greek word *thallos*, meaning green shoot because it shows a green line when examined in a spectrometer
Shell pattern of electrons: 2–8–18–32–18–3

Biology

Thallium is not found in living things, but it can be absorbed by the skin, and it then builds up in the body, affecting the nervous system. It was once used as a medicine for treating ringworm and skin infections. Because it can be extremely toxic to people, many applications of the element have been stopped.

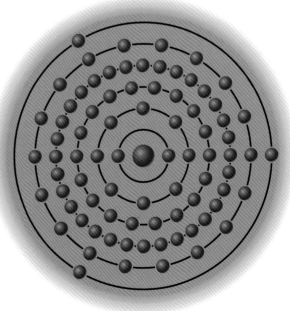

Thorium (Th)

Element 90. A silvery-white radioactive metal in the actinide series on the Periodic Table. Thorium metal does not oxidize easily; but when a small amount of thorium oxide is present, it oxidizes quickly in air to a black color. Thorium oxide has the highest melting point of all oxides (3,300°C).

Key facts...
Name: thorium
Symbol: Th
Atomic number: 90
Atomic weight: 232
Position in Periodic Table: inner transition metal; period 7 (actinide series)
State at room temperature: solid
Color: silvery-white
Density of solid: 11.66 g/cc
Melting point: 1,750°C
Boiling point: 4,780°C
Origin of name: named for Thor, the mythological Scandinavian god of war
Shell pattern of electrons: 2–8–18–32–18–10–2

▲ Thorium oxide accounts for the brilliant white glow of these gas mantles.

Geology

Thorium is not found as a native metal. The main thorium ores are thorite and thorianite. Most thorite is found in the mineral monazite sand with other rare earths.

Biology

Thorium is not found in living things. Since it is radioactive, it is a source of danger to people exposed to it in unshielded environments.

Technology

Thorium is added to magnesium alloys to improve their high-temperature strength. Thorium can be a source of nuclear power. The potential heat energy from thorium is greater than that of uranium and fossil fuels combined. The radioactive heating in the Earth's core may be mainly due to thorium.

Thorium oxide is used to impregnate camping lantern gas mantles and accounts for their brilliant white light. The oxide is also used for making high-quality camera lenses.

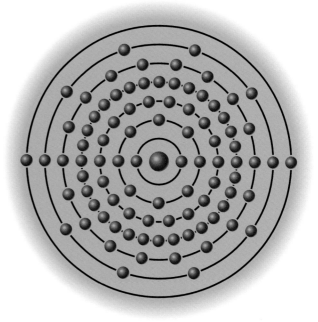

Thulium (Tm)

Element 69. Once thought of as the rarest member of the rare–earth metals (lanthanides) on the Periodic Table, new ores have recently been found, and it is now thought of as being about as rare as silver, gold, or cadmium.

The metal is silvery colored, very soft, and can be cut with a knife. It is easily worked. It does not readily corrode in dry air but quickly decomposes in damp air or water.

Discovery

Thulium was discovered in Sweden in 1879 by Per Teodor Cleve.

Technology

Thulium has few uses because it is very expensive to isolate. Thulium can be isolated by reduction of the oxide with lanthanum metal. New refining techniques are making it cheaper to extract and therefore a more attractive option for some uses. It is incorporated in some alloys. Artificially radioactive thulium is used in small portable X-ray machines. Isotopes of thulium have potential as nuclear energy sources and as the ferrites (ceramic magnetic materials) in microwave equipment.

Geology

Thulium is never found as the native metal, but occurs in complex minerals of gadolinite, monazite sand, and bastnasite. The main economically useful ore is monazite, and even it contains only about 0.007% of the element by volume.

Key facts...
Name: thulium
Symbol: Tm
Atomic number: 69
Atomic weight: 168.9
Position in Periodic Table: inner transition metal; period 6 (lanthanide series)
State at room temperature: solid
Color: silvery
Density of solid: 9.31 g/cc
Melting point: 1,545°C
Boiling point: 1,727°C
Origin of name: named for Thule, an ancient word for Scandinavia
Shell pattern of electrons: 2–8–18–31–8–2

Biology

Thulium is not found in living things. It is regarded as a toxic substance.

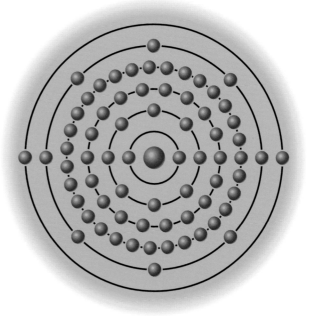

Tin (Sn)

Element 50. Tin is a soft, silvery-white or gray metal in group 4 (the carbon group) on the Periodic Table. Tin can easily be worked, but it has no strength. Silvery colored tin is crystalline. When it is bent, the crystal lattices break, resulting in a sound that is like a scream. The gray form only occurs below 13.2°C. As a result, silvery tin can become gray in cold conditions. The change can be stopped by alloying with small amounts of antimony or bismuth. Tin has been known since earliest times, when it was alloyed with copper to make bronze. Tin is highly resistant to corrosion because, on exposure to air, it forms a thin film of tin oxide on its surface. Tin has a low melting point.

Key facts...
Name: tin
Symbol: Sn
Atomic number: 50
Atomic weight: 118.7
Position in Periodic Table: group 4 (14) (carbon group); period 5
State at room temperature: solid
Color: silvery-white or gray
Densities of solids: (white form) 7.28 g/cc; (gray form) 5.75 g/cc
Melting point: 231.97°C
Boiling point: 2,270°C
Origin of name: from the Anglo-Saxon word *tin*; the symbol Sn is from the Latin word *stannum*, meaning tin
Shell pattern of electrons: 2–8–18–18–4

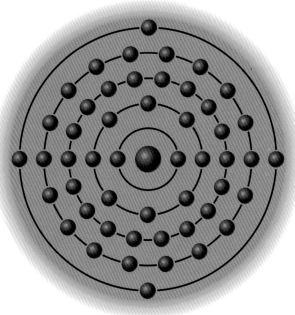

Discovery

It is a very soft material on its own and had few uses; but when alloyed with copper, it produced harder bronze, hence beginning the Bronze Age, one of the most fundamental eras of human civilization.

◀ If the tin plating on a tin can is stratched, the steel beneath is left vulnerable to corrosion.

Technology

Its low reactivity and widespread occurrence have made it an important metal for coating on other metals to prevent corrosion. The term tin can means a tin-plated steel can. Tin has also been used on baking dishes.

Tin is a weak metal and is not used for any form of construction. Alloys that are made with tin include solder, pewter, bronze, and bell metal. Tin compounds are sprayed onto glass to make the glass surface conduct electricity. Plate (window) glass is made by floating molten glass on a bed of molten tin. Wire of tin-niobium alloys makes much more powerful magnets than those made using copper wire. Tin compounds have also been used on ship hulls to prevent the growth of barnacles. However, this use is being discontinued for environmental reasons.

Geology

Tin is not found as the native metal, but mainly in the tin ore cassiterite (tin oxide, SnO_2). Cassiterite occurs in hydrothermal veins close to ancient volcanoes.

Biology

Tin is a trace element in some animals, but tin compounds are mainly toxic to animals, bacteria, and fungi. That is why they can be used as bactericides and fungicides.

▼ Cassiterite is the principal ore of tin.

◀ The Margate Elephant, New Jersey, was made out of tin to resisit the corrosive effects of the sea air.

For more on tin, see Volume 10: Lead and Tin in the *Elements* set.

Titanium (Ti)

Element 22. Titanium is a silvery-gray metal belonging to the transition metals on the Periodic Table.

It has a low density and great strength. Titanium has the strength of steel, but is far lighter. It also resists corrosion as well as platinum.

Titanium is a good reflector of infrared radiation. It burns in air.

Pure titanium dioxide is almost transparent and reflects light as diamond does.

Key facts...
Name: titanium
Symbol: Ti
Atomic number: 22
Atomic weight: 47.87
Position in Periodic Table: transition metal, group (4) (titanium group); period 4
State at room temperature: solid
Color: silvery-gray
Density of solid: 4.5 g/cc
Melting point: 1,660°C
Boiling point: 3,287°C
Origin of name: named for the Titans (the sons of the Earth goddess in Greek mythology)
Shell pattern of electrons: 2–8–10–2

Discovery

It was discovered in 1791 by the English chemist and mineralogist the Reverend William Gregor. He first called the element menachanite after Menaccan in Cornwall, England. It was later renamed titanium.

Technology

Alloyed with other metals such as aluminum, molybdenum, and iron, it adds strength and the ability to stand up to both high and low temperatures with less risk of metal fatigue. It goes into aircraft fuselages, ship propellers, and replacement hips. The reflective properties are applied in solar observatories. It can make synthetic gemstones or, as compounds, paint and fireworks.

Geology

Titanium does not occur as the native element. It is the ninth most abundant element in the Earth's crust. It is found in most igneous rocks, particularly in rutile (titanium oxide, TiO_2) and ilmenite (iron titanium oxide, $FeTiO_3$).

Biology

Titanium is not found in living things.

◄ This blade is razor sharp and can cut palm-oil nut clusters. The metal is titanium, which came from the fuselage of a fighter jet.

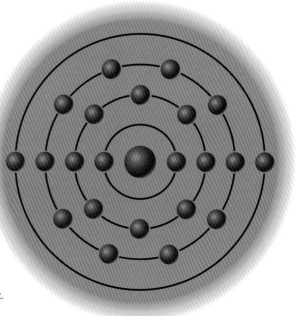

Tungsten (W)

Element 74. Tungsten was formerly called wolfram. It is a white to grayish metal belonging to the transition metals on the Periodic Table.

It is the strongest metal known at high temperatures, and it also has the highest melting point of all metals. Tungsten oxidizes in air, but the thin oxide film that forms then protects it from further corrosion. It is resistant to attack by acids. It has about the same coefficient of expansion as laboratory glass.

Key facts...

Symbol: tungsten
Symbol: W
Atomic number: 74
Atomic weight: 183.8
Position in Periodic Table: transition metal, group (6) (chromium group); period 6
State at room temperature: solid
Color: grayish-white
Density of solid: 19.3 g/cc
Melting point: 3,410°C
Boiling point: 5,660°C
Origin of name: from the Swedish words *tung* (heavy) and *sten* (stone). The symbol W is from wolfram, named for the tungsten mineral wolframite.
Shell pattern of electrons: 2–8–18–32–12–2

Discovery

It was discovered in 1783 by the Spanish chemist brothers Juan José and Fausto Elhuyar.

Technology

It is used as an alloy with steel and in the filaments of bulbs, as well as for the elements in electric furnaces. As tungsten carbide it goes into drill bits. It can be used with glass in the laboratory because it expands at about the same rate as laboratory glassware.

Tungsten salts are part of fluorescent lighting and hide tanning.

Geology

Tungsten is not found as the native element. The main mineral containing tungsten is wolframite (iron–manganese tungstate, $FeMnWO_4$).

Biology

Tungsten is an important trace element.

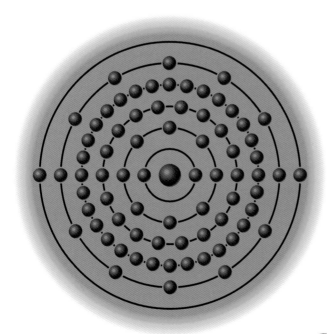

▶ The filament in a household light bulb is made of tungsten, which can glow white hot without burning. About a meter of tungsten wire is coiled up like a spring to make the filament in a standard bulb.

Ununbium (Uub)

Element 112. It is one of the most recently discovered elements, and very little is so far known about it. Only a few atoms of element 112 have ever been made. That was done by fusing a zinc atom with a lead atom by accelerating the zinc atom to high energies in a heavy ion accelerator. Ununbium can also be obtained as part of the decay sequence of ununoctium.

Atoms of this element have a life of less than a millisecond.

Discovery

Element 112 was discovered in 1996 by S. Hofmann, V. Ninov, F. P. Hessberger, P. Armbruster, H. Folger, G. Münzenberg, and others at Darmstadt, Germany. Ununbium is a temporary name and will be changed when international agreement has been reached.

Technology

So little of it has been produced that it has no uses.

Geology

It does not occur naturally in the environment.

Biology

It does not occur in living things.

Key facts...

Name: ununbium
Symbol: Uub
Atomic number: 112
Atomic weight: 277
Position in Periodic Table: transition metal, group (12) (zinc group); period 7
State at room temperature: n/a
Color: unknown
Density: n/a
Melting point: n/a
Boiling point: n/a
Origin of name: so far this element has only been given a temporary name according to an international scheme of established scientific procedures
Shell pattern of electrons: 2–8–18–32–32–18–2

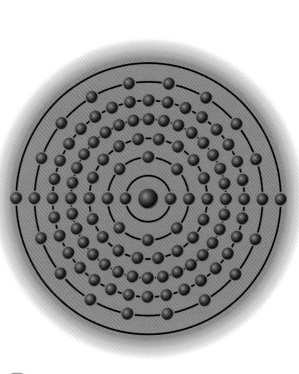

Ununhexium (Uuh)

Element 116. It is one of the most recently discovered elements, and very little is so far known about it. Only a few atoms of element 116 have ever been made, and they are only a brief product of the decay of element 118 (see ununoctium). Element 118 decays less than a millisecond after its formation to make element 116, which then decays in a similarly short time to element 114 (ununquadium).

Discovery

Ununhexium was discovered in 1999 by V. Ninov, K. E. Gregorich, W. Loveland, A. Ghiorso, D.C. Hoffman, D. M. Lee, H. Nitsche, W. J. Swiatecki, U. W. Kirbach, C. A. Laue, J. L. Adams, J. B. Patin, D. A. Shaughnessy, D. A. Strellis, and P. A. Wilk at Berkeley, California.

   Ununhexium is a temporary name and will be changed when international agreement has been reached.

Technology

So little of it has been produced that it has no uses.

Geology

It does not occur naturally in the environment.

Biology

It does not occur in living things.

Key facts...

Name: ununhexium
Symbol: Uuh
Atomic number: 116
Atomic weight: 289
Position in Periodic Table: group 6 (16) (oxygen group or chalcogen); period 7
State at room temperature: not known, but probably a solid
Color: unknown
Density: n/a
Melting point: n/a
Boiling point: n/a
Origin of name: so far this element has only been given a temporary name according to an international scheme of established scientific procedures
Shell pattern of electrons: 2–8–18–32–32–18–6

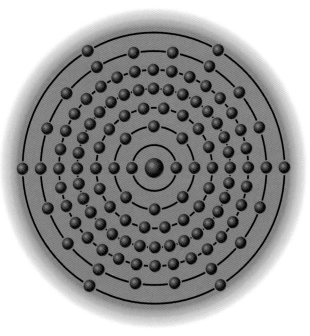

Ununnilium (Uun)

Element 110. It is one of the most recently discovered elements, and very little is so far known about it. Only a few atoms of element 110 have ever been made, although it is expected that its properties are similar to those of platinum, except for the fact that element 110 is unstable and decays in a millisecond.

Those atoms that were made were produced by the nuclear fusion of an isotope of lead with one of nickel using a heavy ion accelerator. Many billion billion nickel atoms were fired at a lead target in order to produce a single atom of element 110. That took many days.

Discovery

Discovered by S. Hofmann, V. Ninov, F. P. Hessberger, P. Armbruster, H. Folger, G. Münzenberg, H. J. Schött, and others at Darmstadt, Germany, in November 1994. Ununnilium is a temporary name and will be changed when international agreement has been reached.

Technology

So little of it has been produced that it has no uses.

Geology

It does not occur naturally in the environment.

Biology

It does not occur in living things.

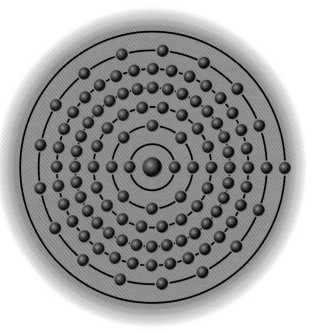

Ununoctium (Uuo)

Element 118. It is one of the most recently discovered elements, and very little is so far known about it. Only a few atoms of element 118 have ever been made. The experiment was carried out using calculations by Robert Smolanczuk (Soltan Institute for Nuclear Studies, Poland) about the fusion of atomic nuclei.

The atoms were produced by fusing a krypton-86 ion with lead-208 atom using an accelerator. That produced 449 million electron volts whose beam was directed onto targets of lead-208. It took 11 days to produce 3 atoms, which then decomposed in under a millisecond (ms) to element 116, ununhexium. One atom of element 118 is produced in every 1,012 interactions between krypton and lead.

Discovery

It was discovered in 1999 by V. Ninov, K. E. Gregorich, W. Loveland, A. Ghiorso, D. C. Hoffman, D. M. Lee, H. Nitsche, W. J. Swiatecki, U. W. Kirbach, C. A. Laue, J. L. Adams, J. B. Patin, D. A. Shaughnessy, D. A. Strellis, and P. A. Wilk at Berkeley, California.

Technology

So little of it has been produced that it has no uses.

Geology

It does not occur naturally in the environment.

Biology

It does not occur in living things.

Key facts...

Name: ununoctium
Symbol: Uuo
Atomic number: 118
Atomic weight: 293
Position in Periodic Table: group 8 (18), (noble gases); period 7
State at room temperature: not known, but probably a gas
Color: unknown
Density: n/a
Melting point: n/a
Boiling point: n/a
Origin of name: so far this element has only been given a temporary name according to an international scheme of established scientific procedures.
Shell pattern of electrons: 2–8–18–32–32–18–8

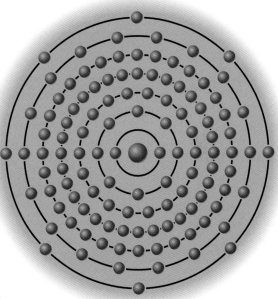

$$^{293}_{118}\text{Uuo} \longrightarrow {}^{289}_{116}\text{Uuh} + 42\text{He} \ (0.12 \text{ ms})$$

$$^{289}_{116}\text{Uuh} \longrightarrow {}^{285}_{114}\text{Uuq} + 42\text{He} \ (0.60 \text{ ms})$$

$$^{285}_{114}\text{Uuq} \longrightarrow {}^{281}_{112}\text{Uub} + 42\text{He} \ (0.58 \text{ ms})$$

$$^{281}_{112}\text{Uub} \longrightarrow {}^{277}_{110}\text{Uun} + 42\text{He} \ (0.89 \text{ ms})$$

$$^{277}_{110}\text{Uun} \longrightarrow {}^{273}_{108}\text{Hs} + 42\text{He} \ (3 \text{ ms})$$

$$^{273}_{108}\text{Hs} \longrightarrow {}^{269}_{106}\text{Sg} + 42\text{He} \ (1,200 \text{ ms})$$

Ununquadium (Uuq)

Element 114. It is one of the most recently discovered elements, and very little is so far known about it. Only a few atoms of element 114 have ever been made. These atoms were produced by nuclear fusion of a calcium atom with a plutonium atom. It is also produced as part of the natural decay sequence of ununoctium. It lasts for just a fraction of a second.

Discovery

It was discovered by workers at the Nuclear Institute at Dubna, Russia, December 1998.

Ununquadium is a temporary name and will be changed when international agreement has been reached.

Technology

So little of it has been produced that it has no uses.

Geology

It does not occur naturally in the environment.

Biology

It does not occur in living things.

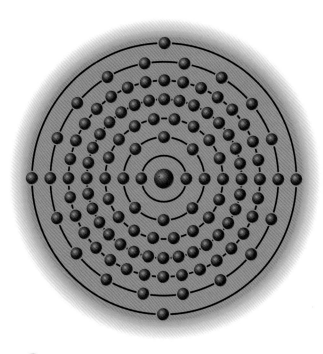

Unununium (Uuu)

Element 111. It is one of the most recently discovered elements, and very little is so far known about it. Only a few atoms of element 111 have ever been made. That involved the nuclear fusion of an isotope of bismuth with one of nickel using a heavy ion accelerator.

Discovery

Unununium was discovered on December 8, 1994, at Darmstadt in Germany by S. Hofmann, V. Ninov, F. P. Hessberger, P. Armbruster, H. Folger, G. Münzenberg, and others.

Unununium is a temporary name and will be changed when international agreement has been reached.

Technology

So little of it has been produced that it has no uses.

Geology

It does not occur naturally in the environment.

Biology

It does not occur in living things.

Key facts...

Name: unununium
Symbol: Uuu
Atomic number: 111
Atomic weight: 272
Position in Periodic Table: transition metal, group (11) (copper group); period 7
State at room temperature: n/a
Color: unknown
Density: n/a
Melting point: n/a
Boiling point: n/a
Origin of name: so far this element has only been given a temporary name according to an international scheme of established scientific procedures
Shell pattern of electrons: 2–8–18–32–32–18–1

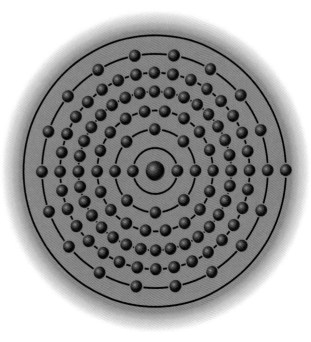

Uranium (U)

Element 92. The best-known element in the actinide series on the Periodic Table associated with radioactivity.

Uranium is a dense, hard, silvery-white metal that can easily be shaped.

During the 1930s it was realized that uranium could be bombarded by slow neutrons and so cause a chain reaction leading to a nuclear explosion. That is the basis of the atomic bomb.

Key facts...
Name: uranium
Symbol: U
Atomic number: 92
Atomic weight: 238
Position in Periodic Table: inner transition metal; period 6 (actinide series)
State at room temperature: solid
Color: silvery-white
Density of solid: 19.05 g/cc
Melting point: 1,132.3°C
Boiling point: 3,818°C
Origin of name: named for the planet Uranus, which had recently been discovered
Shell pattern of electrons: 2–8–18–32–21–9–2

▲ A uranium billet for reprocessing.

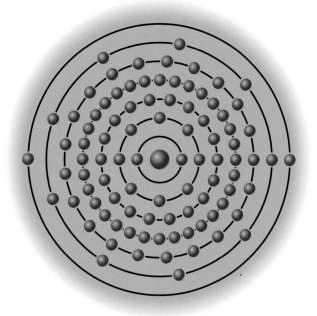

Discovery

It was discovered in Germany in 1789 by Martin Heinrich Klaproth. Although it was discovered in the 18th century, it was not until 1896 that the French physicist Henri Becquerel discovered that uranium was radioactive.

Technology

Its main use is as a nuclear fuel because a kilogram of uranium produces the same energy as three million kilograms of coal. It can be converted into plutonium in "breeder" reactors. It is also used in nuclear bombs.

Geology

The most important uranium ore is uranite, usually called pitchblende, UO_2. Most of the Earth's internal heat is probably caused by nuclear reactions of uranium (and thorium).

Biology

Uranium does not occur in living things. It is now found in small concentrations in places where nuclear explosions or leaks have occurred. Uranium is radioactive and is therefore a radiation hazard.

For more on uranium, see Volume 15: Uranium and Other Radioactive Elements in the *Elements* set.

Vanadium (V)

Element 23. A silvery-white soft metal belonging to the transition metals on the Periodic Table. It resists corrosion by acids and alkalis.

Discovery

Vanadium was discovered independently in Mexico in 1801 by Andres Manuel del Rio and again in Sweden in 1831 by Nils Sefström.

Technology

It can be alloyed with steel to make strong drill bits. It can also go into rust-resistant steel. Vanadium makes high-temperature steels and also helps in the alloying of other metals. Vanadium can also be a catalyst for speeding up chemical reactions. Because of their colors, vanadium compounds are used for dyeing fabrics.

Geology

It does not occur as a native metal, but appears in many minerals, including vanadite, also known as brown lead and carnotite. It is found in coal and crude oil.

Biology

Vanadium is an essential trace element for some animals, especially birds. Lack of vanadium stunts growth. It is also found in sea squirts.

Key facts...

Name: vanadium
Symbol: V
Atomic number: 23
Atomic weight: 50.9
Position in Periodic Table: transition metal, group (5) (vanadium group); period 4
State at room temperature: solid
Color: silvery-white
Density of solid: 5.96 g/cc
Melting point: 1,890°C
Boiling point: 3,380°C
Origin of name: named for Vanadis, the goddess of beauty and youth in Scandinavian mythology. This was suggested by the range of beautiful colors that are produced by vanadium compounds.
Shell pattern of electrons: 2–8–11–2

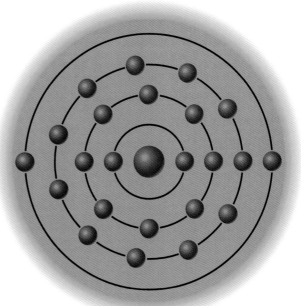

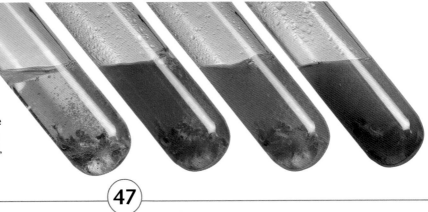

▶ Like many other transition elements, vanadium has several different oxidation states due to the electron arrangement of its atoms. In this series the changes in oxidation state are shown by associated colors from an oxidation state of 5 (yellow), to 4 (blue), to 3 (green), and finally to 2 (violet).

Xenon (Xe)

Element 54. Xenon is one of the noble gases, group 8 on the Periodic Table.

It is a very rare, heavy gas that is colorless, odorless, and tasteless. Only one part of air in twenty million is xenon. However, it is more plentiful in some mineral springs. It also exists in the Martian atmosphere. It is recovered commercially by liquefying air.

Xenon is one of the "inert" gases: It is remarkably unreactive and mainly only forms compounds with fluorine, which is the most reactive nonmetal known. Xenon compounds with metals are known as perxenates.

Some of the rare compounds that have been produced in the laboratory include compounds such as sodium perxenate, xenon difluoride, xenon tetrafluoride, and xenon hexafluoride. The perxenates are used as oxidizing agents in laboratories.

Discovery

Xenon was discovered in 1898 by the British chemists Sir William Ramsay and Morris W. Travers as they evaporated liquid air to find out what it was made of.

Key facts...

Name: xenon
Symbol: Xe
Atomic number: 54
Atomic weight: 131.29
Position in Periodic Table: group 8 (18) (noble gases); period 5
State at room temperature: gas
Color: colorless
Density of gas at 20°C: 5.49 g/l
Melting point: -111.9°C
Boiling point: -107.1°C
Origin of name: from the Greek word *xenos*, meaning stranger
Shell pattern of electrons: 2–8–18–18–8

Technology

When xenon is excited by an electric charge in a vacuum, it gives off a blue glow, which is a source of strobe lights, high-speed photography bulbs, and bulbs that kill bacteria.

Geology

Xenon makes up a tiny part of the air (0.01 part per million). It is four and a half times as heavy as air.

Biology

Xenon is not found in living things. The element itself is not harmful, but its compounds are very toxic because the only compounds it makes are with extremely powerful oxidizing agents.

For more on xenon, see Volume 1: Hydrogen and the Noble Gases in the *Elements* set.

Ytterbium (Yb)

Element 70. A metal belonging to the rare-earth metals (lanthanides) on the Periodic Table. It has a bright silvery luster and is soft and easily worked. It corrodes quite easily in air and water, and needs to be kept in closed containers to protect it from air and moisture. It reacts easily with acids.

Discovery

Discovered in Switzerland in 1878 by Jean-Charles Galinard de Marignac, who named it for the Swedish town of Ytterby. In 1907 and 1908 Georges Urbain of France and Carl Auer von Welsbach of Austria independently separated ytterbium into two elements. One of them remained named ytterbium, while the other was called lutetium.

Technology

Ytterbium can be used as an alloy to improve the strength of stainless steel. It can also go into magnetic materials. It has also been a radiation source for portable X-ray machines.

Geology

Ytterbium is not found as a native element, but in gadolinite, euxenite, and xenotime ores with other rare-earth elements. It is the 44th most abundant element in the Earth's surface rocks.

Biology

Ytterbium is not found in living things.

Key facts...
Name: ytterbium (originally called ytterbia)
Symbol: Yb
Atomic number: 70
Atomic weight: 173
Position in Periodic Table: inner transition metal; period 6 (lanthanide series)
State at room temperature: solid
Color: silvery
Density of solid: 6.97 g/cc
Melting point: 824°C
Boiling point: 1,193°C
Origin of name: named for the town of Ytterby in Sweden
Shell pattern of electrons: 2–8–18–32–8–2

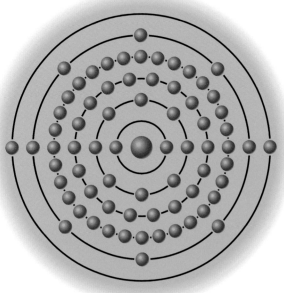

Yttrium (Y)

Element 39. A silvery-colored metal belonging to the rare-earth metals (lanthanides) on the Periodic Table. Powdered yttrium ignites spontaneously in air.

Discovery

Discovered by the Finnish scientist Johan Gadolin (whose name is remembered in the element gadolinium) in 1794. However, the element was isolated by Carl Gustav Mosander only in 1843.

First called yttria, for the nearby town of Ytterby, Sweden (a rich source of many rare-earth minerals), it was subsequently renamed yttrium. It was the first rare earth to be discovered.

Technology

Yttrium is used in metal alloys, and yttrium oxide makes the red dots (phosphors) on color television tubes.

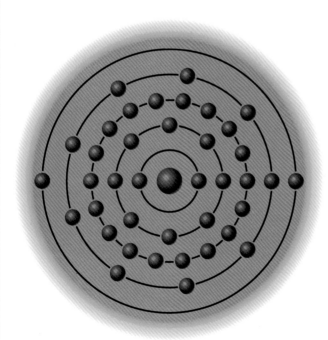

Yttrium aluminum garnet is a gemstone that looks like a diamond. It is also used in glass and ceramics because it helps make them shock-resistant. It has a coefficient of expansion similar to glass. Yttrium can be a catalyst and goes into alloys to increase the strength of metals such as chromium. Radioactive yttrium can treat cancer.

Geology

Yttrium is never found as a native element, but mainly combined with other rare earths in the minerals gadolinite, euxenite, and xenotime. Yttrium was also found in samples of lunar rock collected on the Apollo missions.

Biology

Yttrium is not found in living things. It is, however, not thought to be harmful.

Zinc (Zn)

Element 30. A soft, easily shaped, blue-gray metal. Although zinc is found in the block of transition metals on the Periodic Table, it does not show the typical properties of those elements. It has a much lower melting point, and the majority of its compounds are colorless. It is brittle at room temperature but easily bent and shaped above the boiling point of water. It is a good conductor of electricity and heat. When it burns, it gives off white clouds of zinc oxide.

Discovery

Zinc was discovered by Andreas Marggraf in Germany in 1500.

Technology

Zinc was used for thousands of years before it was identified as an element. It has been alloyed with copper to produce brass since ancient times. Brass contains

Key facts...
Name: *zinc*
Symbol: Zn
Atomic number: 30
Atomic weight: 65.39
Position in Periodic Table: transition metal, group (12) (zinc group); period 4
State at room temperature: solid
Color: blue-gray
Density of solid: 7.13 g/cc
Melting point: 419°C
Boiling point: 907°C
Origin of name: from the German word *zink*
Shell pattern of electrons: 2–8–18–2

Pieces of zinc

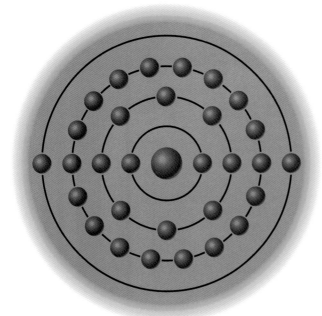

between 20 and 45% zinc, making a variety of types of brass. Brass is harder than zinc and is a good conductor of electricity. It is used for pins and contacts in switches, plugs, and sockets. Bronze and solder also contain zinc, as do cheap dry batteries (zinc-carbon batteries).

Zinc forms a protective coating for steel, the combination being called galvanized iron. Zinc is attached to many iron structures to protect them. When securely fastened to iron, the zinc corrodes, leaving the iron untouched. In this role the zinc is called a sacrificial anode.

Zinc is in some coins. The penny (one-cent) coin is zinc plated with bronze.

Zinc oxide makes paints, rubber, cosmetics, and medicines (as ointment). Zinc sulfide makes luminous dials for watches and fluorescent lights.

Geology

Zinc is never found as a native element, but is common as a sulfide. Zinc ores include sphalerite (zinc sulfide, ZnS) and smithsonite (zinc carbonate, $ZnCO_3$),

Biology

Zinc is an essential trace mineral in plants and animals. It is needed for the production of chemicals called enzymes. A zinc deficiency can stunt growth, and animals with a zinc deficiency need far more food to grow than if they are fed the correct amount of the element.

Although at first glance it appears black, careful inspection reveals that this sphalerite sample is a deep, resinous yellow.

▼ Zinc-based paints
One increasingly important use of zinc is in the form of high-purity powder called zinc dust. It can be incorporated in corrosion-resistant paints and other coatings. This picture shows a zinc-painted section of the Sydney Harbour Bridge, Australia.

For more on zinc, see Volume 6: Zinc, Cadmium, and Mercury in the *Elements* set.

Zirconium (Zr)

Element 40. A soft, silvery-white metal belonging to the transition metals on the Periodic Table. Zirconium powder can catch fire (combust) spontaneously in air. Zirconium resists attack by acids and alkalis. An alloy of zirconium and zinc is magnetic at very low temperatures.

Discovery

Zirconium was identified in 1789 in the mineral zircon by the German chemist Martin Heinrich Klaproth. It was isolated as an element in 1824 by the Swedish chemist Jöns Jacob Berzelius.

Technology

Crystals of zirconium oxide appear in jewelry as a substitute for diamond, where it is known as cubic zirconium. It is also used as a structural material for nuclear reactors, because it is highly transparent to neutrons, and as an alloy with magnesium and steel. Since it resists corrosion, it is widely applied in the chemical and power industries. It is also used for surgical implants. Zirconium is a superconductor at low temperatures. It is used in the form of a zirconium-niobium alloy. Zirconium also makes bulb filaments.

Geology

Zirconium is not found as a native element. It occurs in the mineral zircon ($ZrSiO_4$), which is gold colored.

Biology

Zirconium is not found in living things.

Key facts...
Name: zirconium
Symbol: Zr
Atomic number: 40
Atomic weight: 91.22
Position in Periodic Table: transition metal, group (4) (titanium group); period 5
State at room temperature: solid
Color: silvery-white
Density of solid: 6.49 g/cc
Melting point: 1,852°C
Boiling point: 4,377°C
Origin of name: from the Arabic word *zargun*, meaning gold color, referring to the color of the mineral zircon
Shell pattern of electrons: 2–8–18–10–2

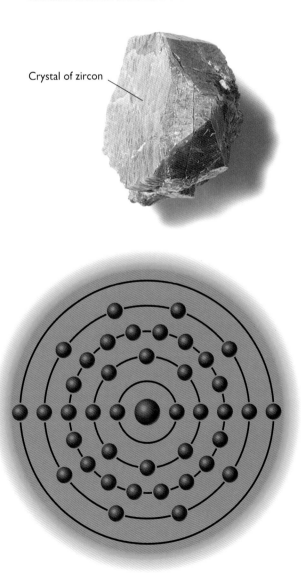

Crystal of zircon

The Periodic Table

Actinium (Ac) 89	Calcium (Ca) 20	Fermium (Fm) 100
Aluminum (Al) 13	Californium (Cf) 98	Fluorine (F) 9
Antimony (Sb) 51	Carbon (C) 6	Francium (Fr) 87
Americium (Am) 95	Cerium (Ce) 58	Gadolinium (Gd) 64
Argon (Ar) 18	Cesium (Cs) 55	Gallium (Ga) 31
Arsenic (As) 33	Chlorine (Cl) 17	Germanium (Ge) 32
Astatine (At) 85	Chromium (Cr) 24	Gold (Au) 79
Barium (Ba) 56	Cobalt (Co) 27	Hafnium (Hf) 72
Berkelium (Bk) 97	Copper (Cu) 29	Hassium (Hs) 108
Beryllium (Be) 4	Curium (Cm) 96	Helium (He) 2
Bismuth (Bi) 83	Dubnium (Db) 105	Holmium (Ho) 67
Bohrium (Bh) 107	Dysprosium (Dy) 66	Hydrogen (H) 1
Boron (B) 5	Einsteinium (Es) 99	Indium (In) 49
Bromine (Br) 35	Erbium (Er) 68	Iodine (I) 53
Cadmium (Cd) 48	Europium (Eu) 63	Iridium (Ir) 77

GROUPS ▶

PERIODS ▼

Transition metals

	1 (1)	2 (2)	(3)	(4)	(5)	(6)	(7)	(8)
1	1 **H** Hydrogen 1							
2	3 **Li** Lithium 7	4 **Be** Beryllium 9						
3	11 **Na** Sodium 23	12 **Mg** Magnesium 24						
4	19 **K** Potassium 39	20 **Ca** Calcium 40	21 **Sc** Scandium 45	22 **Ti** Titanium 48	23 **V** Vanadium 51	24 **Cr** Chromium 52	25 **Mn** Manganese 55	26 **Fe** Iron 56
5	37 **Rb** Rubidium 85	38 **Sr** Strontium 88	39 **Y** Yttrium 89	40 **Zr** Zirconium 91	41 **Nb** Niobium 93	42 **Mo** Molybdenum 96	43 **Tc** Technetium (99)	44 **Ru** Ruthenium 101
6	55 **Cs** Cesium 133	56 **Ba** Barium 137	71 **Lu** Lutetium 175	72 **Hf** Hafnium 178	73 **Ta** Tantalum 181	74 **W** Tungsten 184	75 **Re** Rhenium 186	76 **Os** Osmium 190
7	87 **Fr** Francium (223)	88 **Ra** Radium (226)	103 **Lr** Lawrencium (260)	104 **Rf** Rutherfordium (261)	105 **Db** Dubnium (262)	106 **Sg** Seaborgium (263)	107 **Bh** Bohrium (262)	108 **Hs** Hassium (265)

■ Metals
□ Metalloids (semimetals)
▨ Nonmetals
▤ Inner transition metals

Lanthanide series

57 **La** Lanthanum 139	58 **Ce** Cerium 140	59 **Pr** Praseodymium 141	60 **Nd** Neodymium 144

Actinide series

89 **Ac** Actinium (227)	90 **Th** Thorium (232)	91 **Pa** Protactinium (231)	92 **U** Uranium (238)

Iron (Fe) 26
Krypton (Kr) 36
Lanthanum (La) 57
Lawrencium (Lr) 103
Lead (Pb) 82
Lithium (Li) 3
Lutetium (Lu) 71
Magnesium (Mg) 12
Manganese (Mn) 25
Meitnerium (Mt) 109
Mendelevium (Md) 101
Mercury (Hg) 80
Molybdenum (Mo) 42
Neodymium (Nd) 60
Neon (Ne) 10

Neptunium (Np) 93
Nickel (Ni) 28
Niobium (Nb) 41
Nitrogen (N) 7
Nobelium (No) 102
Osmium (Os) 76
Oxygen (O) 8
Palladium (Pd) 46
Phosphorus (P) 15
Platinum (Pt) 78
Plutonium (Pu) 94
Polonium (Po) 84
Potassium (K) 19
Praseodymium (Pr) 59
Promethium (Pm) 61

Protactinium (Pa) 91
Radium (Ra) 88
Radon (Rn) 86
Rhenium (Re) 75
Rhodium (Rh) 45
Rubidium (Rb) 37
Ruthenium (Ru) 44
Rutherfordium (Rf) 104
Samarium (Sm) 62
Scandium (Sc) 27
Seaborgium (Sg) 106
Selenium (Se) 34
Silicon (Si) 14
Silver (Ag) 47
Sodium (Na) 11

Strontium (Sr) 38
Sulfur (S) 16
Tantalum (Ta) 73
Technetium (Tc) 43
Tellurium (Te) 52
Terbium (Tb) 65
Thallium (Tl) 81
Thorium (Th) 90
Thulium (Tm) 69
Tin (Sn) 50
Titanium (Ti) 22
Tungsten (W) 74
Ununbium (Uub) 112
Ununhexium (Uuh) 116
Ununnilium (Uun) 110

Ununoctium (Uuo) 118
Ununquadium (Uuq) 114
Unununium (Uuu) 111
Uranium (U) 92
Vanadium (V) 23
Xenon (Xe) 54
Ytterbium (Yb) 70
Yttrium (Y) 39
Zinc (Zn) 30
Zirconium (Zr) 40

				3 (13)	4 (14)	5 (15)	6 (16)	7 (17)	8 or 0 (18)
(9)	(10)	(11)	(12)						
									2 He Helium 4
				5 B Boron 11	6 C Carbon 12	7 N Nitrogen 14	8 O Oxygen 16	9 F Fluorine 19	10 Ne Neon 20
				13 Al Aluminum 27	14 Si Silicon 28	15 P Phosphorus 31	16 S Sulfur 32	17 Cl Chlorine 35	18 Ar Argon 40
27 Co Cobalt 59	28 Ni Nickel 59	29 Cu Copper 64	30 Zn Zinc 65	31 Ga Gallium 70	32 Ge Germanium 73	33 As Arsenic 75	34 Se Selenium 79	35 Br Bromine 80	36 Kr Krypton 84
45 Rh Rhodium 103	46 Pd Palladium 106	47 Ag Silver 108	48 Cd Cadmium 112	49 In Indium 115	50 Sn Tin 119	51 Sb Antimony 122	52 Te Tellurium 128	53 I Iodine 127	54 Xe Xenon 131
77 Ir Iridium 192	78 Pt Platinum 195	79 Au Gold 197	80 Hg Mercury 201	81 Tl Thallium 204	82 Pb Lead 207	83 Bi Bismuth 209	84 Po Polonium (209)	85 At Astatine (210)	86 Rn Radon (222)
109 Mt Meitnerium (266)	110 Uun Ununnilium (272)	111 Uuu Unununium (272)	112 Uub Ununbium (277)		114 Uuq Ununquadium (289)		116 Uuh Ununhexium (289)		118 Uuo Ununoctium (293)

61 Pm Promethium (145)	62 Sm Samarium 150	63 Eu Europium 152	64 Gd Gadolinium 157	65 Tb Terbium 159	66 Dy Dysprosium 163	67 Ho Holmium 165	68 Er Erbium 167	69 Tm Thulium 169	70 Yb Ytterbium 173
93 Np Neptunium (237)	94 Pu Plutonium (244)	95 Am Americium (243)	96 Cm Curium (247)	97 Bk Berkelium (247)	98 Cf Californium (251)	99 Es Einsteinium (252)	100 Fm Fermium (257)	101 Md Mendelevium (258)	102 No Nobelium (259)

Understanding equations

As you read through Volumes 1 to 15 in the Elements set, you will notice that many pages contain equations using symbols. Symbols make it easy for chemists to write out the reactions that are occurring in a way that allows a better understanding of the processes involved. If you are not familiar with these symbols, these pages explain them.

Symbols for the elements

The basis for the modern use of symbols for elements dates back to the 19th century. At that time a shorthand was developed using the first letter of the element wherever possible.

Thus O stands for oxygen, H stands for hydrogen, and so on. However, if we were to use only the first letter, there could be some confusion. For example, nitrogen and nickel would both use the symbols N. To overcome this problem, many element symbols take the first two letters of the full name, with the second letter in lowercase. So, although nitrogen is N, nickel becomes Ni. Not all symbols come from the English name; many use the Latin name instead. That is why, for example, gold is not G but Au (from the Latin *aurum*), and sodium has the symbol Na (from the Latin *natrium*).

Compounds of elements are made by combining letters. So, the molecule carbon

Written and symbolic equations

In this book important chemical equations are briefly stated in words (they are called word equations) and are then shown in their symbolic form along with the states.

What reaction the equation illustrates

EQUATION: The formation of calcium hydroxide

Word equation —————— *Calcium oxide + water ⇨ calcium hydroxide*

Symbol equation ————— $CaO(s)$ + $H_2O(l)$ ⇨ $Ca(OH)_2(aq)$

heated

Sometimes you will find additional descriptions below the symbolic equation.

Symbol showing the state:
s is for solid, *l* is for liquid,
g is for gas, and *aq* is for aqueous.

Diagrams

Some of the equations are shown as graphic representations.

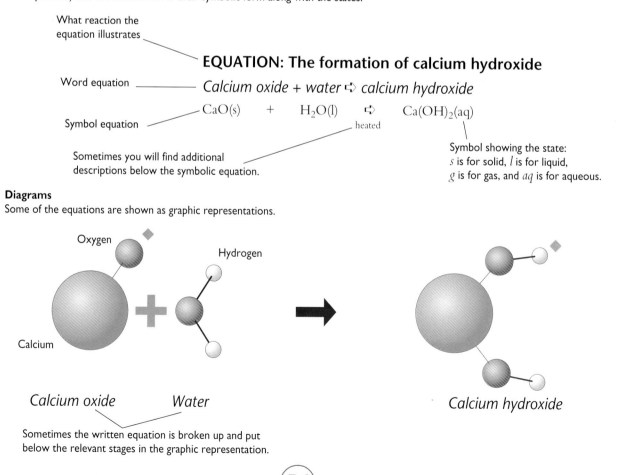

Oxygen

Hydrogen

Calcium

Calcium oxide   *Water*

Sometimes the written equation is broken up and put below the relevant stages in the graphic representation.

Calcium hydroxide

monoxide is CO. By using lowercase letters for the second letter of an element, it is possible to show that cobalt, symbol Co, is not the same as the molecule carbon monoxide, CO.

However, the letters can be made to do much more than this. In many molecules atoms combine in unequal numbers. So, for example, carbon dioxide has one atom of carbon for every two of oxygen. That is shown by using the number 2 beside the oxygen, and the symbol becomes CO_2.

In practice some groups of atoms combine as a unit with other substances. Thus, for example, calcium bicarbonate (one of the compounds used in some antacid pills) is written $Ca(HCO_3)_2$. This shows that the part of the substance inside the parentheses reacts as a unit, and the 2 outside the parentheses shows the presence of two such units.

Some substances attract water molecules to themselves. To show this, a dot is used. So, the blue form of copper sulfate is written $CuSO_4.5H_2O$. In this case five molecules of water attract to one of copper sulfate. When you see the dot, you know that this water can be driven off by heating; it is part of the crystal structure.

In a reaction substances change by rearranging the combinations of atoms. The way they change is shown by using the chemical symbols, placing those that will react (the starting materials, or reactants) on the left and the products of the reaction on the right. Between the two an arrow shows which way the reaction is going.

It is possible to describe a reaction in words. That produces word equations, which are given throughout Volumes 1 to 15. However, it is easier to understand what is happening by using an equation containing symbols. They are also given in many places. They are not shown when the equations are very complex.

In any equation both sides balance; that is, there must be an equal number of like atoms on both sides of the arrow. When you try to write down reactions, you, too, must balance your equation; you cannot have a few atoms left over at the end!

The symbols in parentheses are abbreviations for the physical state of each substance taking part, so that (s) is used for solid, (l) for liquid, (g) for gas, and (aq) for an aqueous solution, that is, a solution of a substance dissolved in water.

Atoms and ions

Each sphere represents a particle of an element. A particle can be an atom or an ion. Each atom or ion is associated with other atoms or ions through bonds – forces of attraction. The size of the particles and the nature of the bonds can be extremely important in determining the nature of the reaction or the properties of the compound.

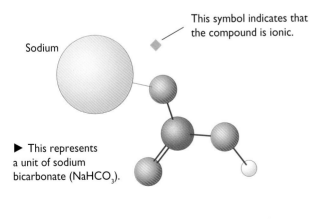

This symbol indicates that the compound is ionic.

Sodium

▶ This represents a unit of sodium bicarbonate ($NaHCO_3$).

The term "unit" is sometimes used to simplify the representation of a combination of ions.

Chemical symbols, equations, and diagrams

The arrangement of any molecule or compound can be shown in one of the two ways shown below, depending on which gives the clearer picture. The left-hand image is called a ball-and-stick diagram because it uses rods and spheres to show the structure of the material. This example shows water, H_2O. There are two hydrogen atoms and one oxygen atom.

Bond shown by "stick"

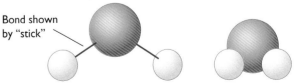

Colors too

The colors of each of the particles help differentiate the elements involved. The diagram can then be matched to the written and symbolic equation given with the diagram. In the case above, oxygen is red, and hydrogen is gray.

Set Index